Grade 3

Grammar
PRACTICE BOOK

Macmillan
McGraw-Hill

The McGraw·Hill Companies

Mc
Graw
Hill **Macmillan
McGraw-Hill**

Published by Macmillan/McGraw-Hill, of McGraw-Hill Education, a division of The McGraw-Hill Companies, Inc.,
Two Penn Plaza, New York, New York 10121.

Printed in the United States of America

8 9 10 006 09 08 07

B

Contents

Unit 2 • Investigations

© Macmillan/McGraw-Hill

Unit 3 • Discoveries

Unit 4 • Determination

© Macmillan/McGraw-Hill

Unit 5 • Challenges

Unit 6 • Achievements

Name_____

> • A **sentence** is a group of words that tells a complete thought.
> • Every sentence begins with a capital letter.
>   Sentence: Peter looked at the building.
>   Not a sentence: At the building.

Write *yes* if the words make a sentence. Write *no* if they do not.

1. Peter's family is moving to a new town. _____

2. Went to a new school. _____

3. Peter worries about his first day. _____

4. Drove him to school. _____

5. He sits quietly in the car. _____

6. Unlike his other school. _____

7. Bigger and newer. _____

8. Felt lost. _____

9. Then he saw his classroom. _____

10. Bright and sunny. _____

11. Made friends. _____

12. Peter had a lot of fun. _____

13. Peter's new teacher. _____

14. Not nervous. _____

15. He can't wait to go back. _____

At Home: Have your child write a few sentences about how he or she felt the first day of school.

First Day Jitters • **Book I/Unit I**   I

Name_____

- A **statement** is a sentence that tells something. It ends with a period.
- A **question** is a sentence that asks something. It ends with a question mark.
  Statement: There are many ways to make new friends.
  Question: What do you do to make friends?

Write *statement* if the sentence tells something. Write *question* if the sentence asks something. Put the correct end mark at the end of the sentence.

1. Meg liked to make new friends _____

2. She said hello to the new student _____

3. How would you greet a new student _____

4. She told him about their school _____

5. She told him how they had fun _____

6. What would you say about your school _____

7. She showed him around the school _____

8. Where would you take a new student _____

9. What would you ask someone new _____

10. Do you like to hear about new places _____

11. We like our school _____

12. What was your school like _____

13. We have a lot of fun reading _____

14. Have fun at your new school _____

At Home: Have your child look at a book or a magazine and point out the sentences that are statements and those that are questions.

Name_____

> • Every sentence begins with a capital letter.
> • A **statement** is a sentence that tells something. It ends with a period.
> • A **question** is a sentence that asks something. It ends with a question mark.
>   Statement: It takes time to learn about a new place.
>   Question: Do you like going to new places?

After each sentence, write *statement* or *question* to identify the kind of sentence it is. Then write the sentence correctly. Use capital letters and end marks.

1. maps can help you find your way _____

   _____

2. do you know how to use a map _____

   _____

3. you can ask others for help _____

   _____

4. can you give me directions _____

   _____

5. do you know where I can find Room 3A _____

   _____

6. soon you will know your way around _____

   _____

7. you will feel right at home _____

   _____

8. will you show others how to find places _____

   _____

 At Home: Have your child write sentences using proper punctuation.

Name_____

- A **sentence** is a group of words that tells a complete thought.
- A **statement** is sentence that tells something.
- A **question** is a sentence that asks something.

Read the description of Carly's first day at camp. Circle the mistakes and rewrite the paragraph.

    I woke up early. it was the first day of camp. I didn't know what to expect. Would I know anyone in my group. Would we do things I like to do? Would we swim in the lake or the pool? I had never gone swimming outside before?

    The bus was already filled with campers. I looked nervously down the aisle? Then I saw Lisa. she had been on my soccer team. I sat down next to her. Now I didn't even mind the rain. It would be fine because I had a friend with me.

_____

_____

_____

_____

_____

_____

_____

_____

 At Home: Read the rewritten paragraph with your child and have him or her point out the statements and the questions.

Name

A. Read each group of words. Write *sentence* if the group of words forms a sentence. Write *fragment* if it does not form a sentence.

1. I remember my first day of school. _____

2. Looked strange. _____

3. Was lost. _____

4. I know my way around. _____

5. Have friends. _____

B. Decide if the sentence is a statement or a question. Write your answer on the line. Rewrite the sentence using the correct punctuation and capitalization.

6. do you remember your first day of school _____

_____

7. Maybe you were excited _____

_____

8. maybe you were scared _____

_____

9. Do you know anyone in your class _____

_____

10. did you make new friends _____

_____

11. It seems long ago now _____

_____

12. Do you like your new school _____

_____

Name_____

- A sentence is a group of words that tells a complete thought.
- A **statement** is sentence that tells something.
- A **question** is a sentence that asks something.

Mechanics

- Begin every sentence with a capital letter.
- End a statement with a period.
- End a question with a question mark.

Write each statement or question correctly.

1. today Stan went fishing for the first time

_____

2. it was a perfect day for fishing

_____

3. do you see grandfather's red fishing boat

_____

4. they both wore yellow shirts and blue caps

_____

5. would Stan catch any fish

_____

6. did grandfather remember to bring lunch

_____

- The **subject** of a sentence is whom or what the sentence is about.
- The subject can be one word or more than one word.
  The buildings are tall.
  The office buildings are tall.

What or whom is the sentence about? Draw a line under the subject.

1. The city is my habitat.

2. The streets are busy.

3. The fast cars pass quickly.

4. The park has trees and grass.

5. Tired birds rest in the branches.

6. Squirrels hop through the park.

7. Summers get very hot.

8. Winters are cold and snowy.

9. People rush by quickly.

10. Large buses stop at the corner.

11. The deer runs through the park.

12. Trees lose their leaves.

13. Children play on the playground.

14. The bikes are on the grass.

15. The bus is crowded in the winter.

© Macmillan/McGraw-Hill

 At Home: Have your child write two sentences about where he or she lives. Have your child underline the subject of each sentence.

Whose Habitat Is It?
Book I/Unit I

Name_____

> • Every **sentence** has a subject.
> • The **subject** of a sentence tells what or whom the sentence is about.

Add a subject to each group of words.

1. _____ hopped into the water.

2. _____ was bright and warm.

3. _____ buzzed near the flowers.

4. _____ is orange and black.

5. _____ perched on the branches.

6. _____ drifted across the sky.

7. _____ kept us cool.

8. _____ grew on the trees.

 At Home: Have your child look on the page of a book or magazine and point out the subjects.

© Macmillan/McGraw-Hill

Name_____

A. Write the subject of each sentence.

1. A habitat is where living things live. _____

2. Animals share their habitats with plants. _____

3. People have habitats too. _____

4. The climate is the weather in a habitat. _____

5. Snow is covering my habitat. _____

B. Choose a subject from the box that best completes each sentence. Rewrite the correct sentence.

fish	people	bears
birds	everyone	

6. _____ needs the right kind of habitat.

_____

7. _____ live in trees.

_____

8. _____ find shelter in buildings.

_____

9. _____ swim in lakes and oceans.

_____

10. _____ live in the woods.

_____

Name_____

- The **subject** of a sentence tells what or whom the sentence is about.

Mechanics

- Begin every sentence with a capital letter.
- End every sentence with a special mark.

Read the paragraph and look at the underlined parts. What should you do to correct each part? Rewrite the paragraph fixing any mistakes you find.

The desert is sandy. keeps the desert hot. snakes crawl across the sand do you like snakes Lizards lie on the warm rocks. they sure must like the heat

_____

_____

_____

Name_____

- Every sentence has two parts.
- Every sentence has a subject and a predicate.
- The **predicate** of a sentence tells what the subject does or is.
- The predicate can be one word or more than one word.
  Sentence: The penguins walked across the snow.
  Predicate: <u>walked across the snow.</u>

Which word or words tell what the subject does or is? Draw a line under the predicate.

1. Penguins live in cold climates.

2. A layer of fat keeps penguins warm.

3. Penguins shed their feathers.

4. These big birds grow new feathers.

5. Penguins gather in large groups.

6. They settle along the shore.

7. Many penguins hop over the rocks.

8. The young birds slide along the snow.

9. Penguins dive into the water.

10. Penguins swim very quickly.

© Macmillan/McGraw-Hill

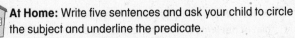
At Home: Write five sentences and ask your child to circle the subject and underline the predicate.

Penguin Chick • **Book I/Unit I** 19

Name_____

- Every sentence has two parts.
- Every sentence has a subject and a predicate.
- The **predicate** of a sentence tells what the subject does or is.

Which word or words tell what the subject does or is? Write the predicate on the line.

1. Ice and snow cover Antarctica.

_____

2. The ice is millions of years old.

_____

3. Temperatures stay below freezing.

_____

4. Cold wind blows across the land.

_____

5. Giant icebergs float in the sea.

_____

6. Seals and penguins live in the cold.

_____

7. Few plants grow in Antarctica.

_____

8. Tourists like to see Antarctica.

_____

 At Home: Give your child a subject, such as snow, and have him or her write five sentences using different predicates.

Name_____

- A sentence is a group of words that tells a complete thought.
- A sentence begins with a capital letter and has an end mark.
- A run-on sentence joins two sentences that should be separate.
    Run-on sentence: It is cold we put on our coats.
    Two sentences: It is cold. We put on our coats.

Read the sentences. Rewrite each run-on to show two sentences.

1. I think snow is beautiful I can't wait for the first snowfall each year!

_____

_____

2. Then it's time to go skiing I also like to skate.

_____

_____

3. Skating outside is fun it's better than skating indoors.

_____

_____

4. I don't mind the cold it makes me feel wide awake.

_____

_____

5. I really like to build snowmen we dress them in funny clothes.

_____

_____

6. I also like to make snow angels I make them all over the grass.

_____

_____

© Macmillan/McGraw-Hill

At Home: Write three run-on sentences. Have your child fix the run-on, circle each subject, and underline each predicate.

Name_____

> • A run-on sentence joins two sentences that should be separate.

Read the paragraphs below. Rewrite the paragraphs using the correct capitalization and punctuation. Be sure to correct each run-on sentence.

My mom loves to visit Antarctica. She goes there every winter she wants me to go with her one day. She travels there for work she is an animal doctor who works with penguins. My mom helps sick penguins feel better she also works with the local animal doctors to help find cures for diseases

One time, my mom got stuck in Antarctica. She could not fly home for a week. I was worried about her, but she called me everyday to tell me that she was okay. Maybe I will go to Antarctica one day with my mom I just do not want to get stuck

_____

_____

_____

_____

_____

_____

_____

_____

_____

_____

At Home: Have a family member write a story with run-on sentences. Ask your child to correct the sentences.

© Macmillan/McGraw-Hill

A. Decide which part of the sentence is the predicate. Circle your answer.

1. The penguin on the shore lost clumps of feathers.
   A. lost clumps of feathers
   B. on the shore
   C. The penguin

2. New feathers filled in the patches.
   A. New feathers
   B. patches
   C. filled in the patches

3. The guide at the zoo showed us the penguins.
   A. showed us the penguins
   B. at the zoo
   C. The guide

4. The penguins in the pool slid down ice hills.
   A. in the pool
   B. slid down ice hills
   C. The penguins

B. Underline the predicate in each sentence.

5. The water around Antarctica is very cold.

6. Seabirds of Antarctica dive for food.

7. The center of Antarctica is called the South Pole.

8. Groups of explorers raced to the South Pole.

- The **predicate** of a sentence tells what the subject does or is.
- A run-on sentence joins two sentences that should be separate.

Mechanics

- Begin every sentence with a capital letter.
- End every sentence with a special mark.

Read the paragraph and look at the underlined parts. What should you do to correct each part? Rewrite the sentences on the lines.

    (1) <u>We are on a cruise to Antarctica it is very interesting.</u> Look at all the wildlife! (2) <u>Giant seals.</u> They bark like dogs! (3) <u>Penguins hop on the rocks they look very funny!</u> (4) <u>Tiny seabirds.</u>

1. _____

_____

2. _____

_____

3. _____

_____

4. _____

_____

© Macmillan/McGraw-Hill

Name_____

> • Two related sentences can be joined with a comma and the word *and* or *but*.
>
>   Separate: Sue has a dog. Tim has a cat.
>   Joined: Sue has a dog, and Tim has a cat.

Combine each pair of sentences. Use a comma and the word *and* or *but*.

1. I like yellow birds. My mother likes green birds.

_____

_____

2. Tame birds eat special bird food. Wild birds like insects.

_____

_____

3. Most birds can sing. Some birds can learn words.

_____

_____

4. Birds can escape from their cages. They can fly around a room.

_____

_____

5. A small bird can sit on your finger. It can even ride on your shoulder.

_____

_____

© Macmillan/McGraw-Hill

 At Home: Have your child look at a book or a magazine for sentences they can combine to make compound sentences.

Name_____

- A sentence that contains two related sentences joined by *and* or *but* is called a **compound sentence**.

Write a compound sentence by joining each pair of sentences. Use a comma and the word *and* or *but*.

1. Hamsters are fun. Goldfish are easier to care for.

   _____

   _____

2. Hamsters are small. Cats are quiet.

   _____

   _____

3. Some hamsters have long hair. Others have short hair.

   _____

   _____

4. Hamsters are small. They can fit in your pocket.

   _____

   _____

5. Some animals stuff food in their cheeks. Hamsters carry it that way.

   _____

   _____

© Macmillan/McGraw-Hill

 At Home: Have your child write two related sentences about a pet they would want using the word *and*.

Name_____

Mechanics

- Use a comma and the word *and* or *but* when joining two sentences to form a compound sentence.
- Begin a compound sentence with a capital letter. End a compound sentence with the correct punctuation.

Read each pair of sentences. Use a comma and the word *and* or *but* to join each pair of sentences.

1. I wanted to choose a pet. It wasn't easy?

_____

_____

2. First I wanted a cat. Then I wanted a dog.

_____

_____

3. Cats don't need baths. They don't need walks.

_____

_____

4. Dogs like to play. They can learn tricks.

_____

_____

5. I talked to Mom and Dad? Then we took a vote.

_____

_____

6. Tomorrow we are going to get a dog. We know exactly what kind.

_____

_____

 At Home: Have your child make a comparison between two things by using compound sentences.

- A sentence that contains two sentences joined by *and* or *but* is called a **compound sentence**.
- Use a comma before *and* or *but* when you join two sentences to form a compound sentence.

Read the paragraph and look for sentences you can combine. Then rewrite the paragraph.

   I observed my cat. Then I studied my dog. My cat is small. He weighs twenty pounds. My dog is big. She weighs fifty pounds. Both like to sleep. Both like to be in the sun. My cat likes to chase birds. He likes to climb. My dog likes to dig. She plays fetch. My cat sleeps on my bed. My dog sleeps on my floor. They are good animals. Both make great pets.

_____

_____

_____

_____

_____

_____

_____

 At Home: Have your child come up with more compound sentences to add to the paragraph about Eddie and Belle.

Name_____

A. Write *yes* or *no* to tell if two sentences have been combined.

1. Some people like having pets, and some people do not want pets.

_____

2. I would like to have more than two cats.

_____

3. I ride my horse each day in the corral.

_____

4. I call my dog, and then he comes to me.

_____

B. Use *and* or *but* to combine each pair of sentences. Write the new sentence on the line. Remember to use a comma where you join the sentences.

5. I have an aquarium. Dad bought some beautiful fish.

_____

_____

6. I have two orange fish. We do not want a blue fish.

_____

_____

7. I feed my fish. Dad cleans the aquarium.

_____

_____

8. I observe my fish. We learn how they live.

_____

_____

Name

- A sentence that contains two sentences joined by *and* or *but* is called a **compound sentence.**
- Use a comma before *and* or *but* when you join two sentences to form a compound sentence.

Mechanics

- Every sentence begins with a capital letter.
- Every sentence ends with a special mark.

Read the paragraph about the picture. First change the underlined sentences to make a compound sentence. Use a comma and the word *and* or *but* to join the sentences. Then write the other sentences correctly on the lines.

there is a pet store in town. it is very busy. the store sells hamsters they have fish we bring our dog Sammy to the store he gets very excited. the store's owner does not like Sammy to bark. he always gives him a treat

_____

_____

_____

_____

Name _____

Read the passage and look at the underlined parts. Is there a mistake? What type of mistake is it? Mark your answer.

It was my first school play. I was very nervous. (1) <u>there was a big audience.</u> They were all watching me. (2) <u>What if I forgot my lines</u> Then the play started. I remembered everything. I was so happy!

1. **A.** Capitalization
   B. Punctuation
   C. Spelling
   D. No mistake

2. **E.** Capitalization
   F. Punctuation
   G. Spelling
   H. No mistake

Every day I get the mail. I look in the mailbox when I get off the bus. (3) <u>I bring the mail inside</u> Then I sort it out. There are envelopes and magazines. Some are for Mom. (4) <u>some are for Dad.</u> Sometimes the mail is for me!

3. **A.** Capitalization
   B. Punctuation
   C. Spelling
   D. No mistake

4. **E.** Capitalization
   F. Punctuation
   G. Spelling
   H. No mistake

(5) <u>What is a habitat!</u> It is the place where an animal or plant lives. Its habitat is the world around it. It is all the other living things there too. (6) <u>it is the kind of weather in that place.</u> It is where that plant or animal belongs.

5. **A.** Capitalization
   B. Punctuation
   C. Spelling
   D. No mistake

6. **E.** Capitalization
   F. Punctuation
   G. Spelling
   H. No mistake

Name _____

Read the passage and look at the underlined parts. Is there a mistake? What would you change to make it sound better? Mark your answer.

    It snowed for the first time today. (7) Covered everything in sight. Ice hung on the trees and the streetlights. (8) The sidewalks. The sun made everything sparkle. I am very happy when it snows.

7. A. Add a subject
   B. Add a predicate
   C. Join two sentences with *and*
   D. No mistake

8. E. Add a subject
   F. Add a predicate
   G. Join two sentences with *and*
   H. No mistake

    Cats are my favorite animal, and my cat is the perfect pet. She is quiet and neat. (9) Plays with string and chases balls. She purrs when I scratch her chin, and she sleeps on my pillow. (10) I love her. She loves me.

9. A. Add a subject
   B. Add a predicate
   C. Join two sentences with *and*
   D. No mistake

10. E. Add a subject
   F. Add a predicate
   G. Join two sentences with *and*
   H. No mistake

Name_____

> • A **noun** names a person, place, or thing.

Write the nouns that appear in each sentence.

1. The boy carried the bags to the car.

_____

2. The workers lifted the boxes onto the truck.

_____

3. Our teacher moved the chairs out of the room.

_____

4. Her friend said she was the strongest student in the class.

_____

5. The twins thought they were each stronger than their brother.

_____

6. The kids had a contest to see who was the strongest.

_____

7. Everyone tried to lift a big rock in the park.

_____

8. Not one person could lift the stone!

_____

At Home: Have your child write three proper nouns that name people he or she knows and three common nouns that name things seen in school.

The Strongest One • **Book I/Unit 2** (**33**)

Name

> • A **common noun** names any person, place, or thing.
> • A **proper noun** names a special person, place, or thing.
> • Begin a proper noun with a capital letter.

Write *common* or *proper* next to the underlined words to identify the type of nouns they are.

1. We have an ant farm in our <u>classroom</u>. _____

2. Let's study the ant farm with <u>Mr. Clark</u>. _____

3. I named my favorite ant <u>Crazy Legs</u>. _____

4. He is fast and could win an ant <u>race</u>. _____

5. Open School Night takes place in <u>October</u>. _____

6. Parents will visit our classroom on <u>Thursday</u>. _____

7. Our teacher will tell them about our <u>classes</u>. _____

8. I plan to show my parents the <u>ant farm</u>! _____

9. My sister and I got some <u>soil</u>. _____

10. My grandparents visited us in <u>September</u>. _____

11. I decided to meet my <u>friends</u>. _____

12. We did not have school on <u>Monday</u>. _____

 At Home: Have your child make lists of common and proper nouns in each category: person, place, and thing.

Name_____

> • A proper noun names a special person, place, or thing and begins with a capital letter.
> • The name of a day, month, or holiday begins with a capital letter

Write the proper nouns that appear in each sentence.

1. We found an anthill on saturday. _____

2. We looked for it again on sunday. _____

3. It kept getting bigger during june. _____

4. More and more ants came during july. _____

5. The busy ants worked hard in august. _____

6. There was less action on labor day. _____

7. The anthill was quiet by halloween. _____

8. It was gone on thanksgiving day. _____

9. Father is off on monday. _____

10. Next month we celebrate mother's day. _____

11. I like spring weather in may. _____

12. We ate pancakes on new year's day. _____

13. We saw fireworks on independence day. _____

14. Squirrels gathered acorns in november. _____

15. It can be very cold on new year's eve. _____

© Macmillan/McGraw-Hill

At Home: Have your child make up sentences that use names of months and holidays.

Name_____

> • Begin a proper noun with a capital letter.
> • Begin the name of a day, month, or holiday with a capital letter.

Look at the underlined nouns. Put a C over common nouns.
Put a P over proper nouns.

The students in <u>ms. harris</u>'s class would like an ant farm. An ant

farm is a good way to learn <u>science</u>. It lets students practice their

observation skills. It shows us how <u>insects</u> live and work. It takes less

care than <u>fish</u> or a guinea pig.

Ant farms are sold at <u>tom's toy shop</u>. The students would like to get one

before <u>thanksgiving</u>.

Writing Activity

**Rewrite the paragraphs so that proper nouns begin with capital
letters and common nouns begin with small letters.**

_____

_____

_____

_____

_____

_____

_____

At Home: Have your child look through a page of a book
or magazine. Tell him or her to make lists of common and
proper nouns.

Name_____

**A. If the underlined noun is a common noun, write common.
If the underlined noun is a proper noun, write proper.**

1. Our class went on a trip to the <u>Museum of Natural History</u>.

   _____

2. We saw a show about <u>insects</u>. _____

3. I thought the <u>spiders</u> were the best part. _____

4. <u>Tracy</u> liked the bees best. _____

5. There are also <u>dinosaurs</u>. _____

6. <u>Robert</u> knows a lot about rainforests. _____

**B. Underline the nouns in each sentence. Put a C over common
nouns. Put a P over proper nouns.**

7. The Fourth of July is my favorite holiday.

8. I love the fireworks that light up the night.

9. We have a big family picnic on July 4.

10. Aunt Claire screamed when ants crawled on her hamburger.

11. There was no school on President's Day.

12. I like to go shopping with Mom on Labor Day.

Name_____

> • A **noun** names a person, place, or thing.
> • A **common noun** names any person, place, or thing.
> • A **proper noun** names a special person, place, or thing.

Mechanics

> • Begin a proper noun with a capital letter.
> • Begin the name of a day, month, or holiday with a capital letter.

Write each sentence correctly.

1. It was very hot on friday afternoon.

_____

2. How long did sam and lisa sit on the porch?

_____

3. Then sam put his cookie down next to him.

_____

4. A group of Ants swarmed around the Cookie!

_____

5. sam did not want to Eat the cookie.

_____

6. Sam and lisa saw more Ants saturday morning.

_____

© Macmillan/McGraw-Hill

Name _____

> - A **singular noun** names one person, place, or thing.
> - A **plural noun** names more than one person, place, or thing.
> - Add -*s* to form the plural of most singular nouns.
> - Add -*es* to form the plural of singular nouns that end in s, ch, sh, or x.

Write the plural form of each singular noun.

1. farm _____

2. fox _____

3. horse _____

4. bucket _____

5. arch _____

6. chicken _____

7. barn _____

8. piece _____

9. wish _____

10. forest _____

Write the plural form of the noun in parentheses to complete each sentence.

11. The library parking lot was filled with (car) _____.

12. Angela walked through the (hall) _____.

13. She showed her sister the new (watch) _____.

14. Angela pointed to the (box) _____.

15. She helped her sound out the (word) _____.

16. One of the books had missing (page) _____.

17. Some scenes have color or black and white (drawing) _____.

18. These pictures are done by her (boss) _____.

© Macmillan/McGraw-Hill

 At Home: Have your child write four singular nouns. Then have him or her turn those nouns into plural nouns.

Wolf! • **Book I/Unit 2** 39

Name_____

- Add -es to form the plural of singular nouns that end in s, sh, ch, or, x.
- To form the plural of nouns ending in a consonant and y, change the y to i and add -es.

Change each word to a plural noun.

1. worry _____   6. path _____

2. wish _____   7. flash _____

3. bench _____   8. porch _____

4. box _____   9. mix _____

5. bus _____   10. kiss _____

Write the plural form of each noun in parentheses.

11. There are several (library) _____.

12. The books are filled with (story) _____.

13. There are trees and (bush) _____ outside the library.

14. You can read under the (branch) _____.

15. I read a story about a wolf that lived with (fox) _____.

16. I was able to read on one of the (bench) _____.

17. Animals can hear you if you step on (stick) _____.

18. Ned found salamanders under several (rock) _____.

19. Look carefully and you'll see a variety of (grass) _____.

20. In the woods, we camped out in (tent) _____.

© Macmillan/McGraw-Hill

 At Home: Have your child make a list of nouns that end in s, x, ch, sh, and y. Then have him or her write the plurals of these nouns.

> • Begin sentences with a capital letter and end them with an end mark.

After each group of words, write statement, question, command, exclamation, or fragment. Rewrite sentences correctly. Use capital letters and end marks.

1. we are going camping in the forest _____

_____

2. many kinds of wildlife _____

_____

3. Will I see a wolf _____

_____

4. wow, that would be exciting _____

_____

5. we waited by the campfire _____

_____

6. was that a howl _____

_____

7. get me my camera _____

_____

8. that's a great wolf picture _____

_____

At Home: Take turns saying sentences aloud with your child. Then have your child write them with the correct end mark.

- Add -*s* to form the plural of most singular nouns.
- Add -*es* to form the plural of singular nouns that end in *s, sh, ch,* or *x.*
- To form the plural of nouns ending in a consonant and *y,* change the *y* to *i* and add -*es.*

On the lines below, write the correct plural version of the underlined nouns from the poster.

_____   _____

_____   _____

_____   _____

Writing Activity

Rewrite the paragraph on the poster. Use the plural versions of the nouns. Make sure every sentence begins with a capital letter and ends with an end mark.

WILD THINGS

You can learn all kinds of wild things at library   you can find fun story   you can discover interesting fact   you can take out movies   And it is all free!   now get wild and go to your library   Get box of book and learn bunch of things

_____

_____

_____

_____

 At Home: Have your child look through a page of a book or magazine. Tell your child to make a list of plural nouns he or she finds.

© Macmillan/McGraw-Hill

Name _____

A. Read the nouns. Find the noun that is singular. Mark your answer.

1. **A.** wolf
   B. lines
   C. yards
   D. buildings

2. **A.** lambs
   B. flower
   C. hills
   D. rivers

3. **A.** houses
   B. streets
   C. letters
   D. chair

4. **A.** girls
   B. boys
   C. students
   D. teacher

B. Read each sentence. Find the correct plural form for the noun in the parentheses.

5. Our (class) all take place in Room 3.
   A. class
   B. classs
   C. classes
   D. classies

6. The wolf read (book) in the garden.
   A. book
   B. bookes
   C. bookess
   D. books

7. There are (couch) in the reading room.
   A. couches
   B. couchs
   C. couch
   D. couchess

8. Then he ate our (peach).
   A. peachs
   B. peaches
   C. peach
   D. peachies

Name_____

- Add -s to form the plural of most singular nouns.
- Add -es to form the plural of singular nouns that end in s, sh, ch, or x.
- To form the plural of nouns ending in a consonant and y, change the y to i and add -es.

Mechanics

- Begin sentences with a capital letter and end them with an end mark.

Rewrite the sentences. Make the underlined nouns plural. Add capital letters and end marks to the sentences.

1. we heard <u>sound</u> in the <u>bush</u>

_____

2. wow, there was a wolf and two <u>fox</u>

_____

3. did we know where there were any <u>library</u>

_____

4. we gave <u>direction</u> to the <u>tourist</u>

_____

5. walk two <u>mile</u> and pass two <u>church</u>

_____

Name_____

> • Some nouns have special plural forms.

Draw a line from each noun to its plural form.

1. foot	women
2. knife	shelves
3. mouse	feet
4. goose	mice
5. child	teeth
6. man	geese
7. woman	lives
8. tooth	men
9. life	children
10. shelf	knives
11. ox	tomatoes
12. leaf	buffalo
13. tomato	oxen
14. buffalo	hooves
15. hoof	leaves

 At Home: Have your child choose four plural nouns from this page. Have him or her use each one in a sentence.

Name

• A few nouns have the same singular and plural forms.

Singular	Plural	Singular	Plural
sheep	sheep	fish	fish
deer	deer	trout	trout
buffalo	buffalo	salmon	salmon
moose	moose	scissors	scissors

Complete each sentence with the correct plural form of the noun in parentheses.

1. In the future, will (buffalo) _____ once again live in the Great Plains?

2. Will (deer) _____ still live in the forests or only in zoos?

3. These wild (horse) _____ lived on their own in the hills.

4. Maybe (fox) _____ will survive in the north.

5. Large schools of (fish) _____ will feed millions of people.

6. Dams must allow (salmon) _____ to swim upstream.

7. People once fished for (trout) _____ for food.

8. Many (dog) _____ run in the fields.

 At Home: Have your child create a story that uses four of the above nouns in both their singular and plural forms.

Name_____

- Some nouns have special plural forms.
- A few nouns have the same singular and plural forms.

Rewrite the sentences. Change the underlined word to a plural noun.

1. The child wondered about the future.

_____

2. People might be able to fly like goose.

_____

3. They might be ten foot tall.

_____

4. They might have more tooth.

_____

5. How else will our life be different?

_____

6. The rivers might run out of fish.

_____

 At Home: Have your child draw a picture showing at least four plural nouns from these sentences. Have your child label the picture of each noun with the correct plural spelling.

- Some nouns have special plural forms.
- A few nouns have the same singular and plural forms.

Proofread the paragraph for incorrect plural nouns. Circle each incorrect plural noun and write its correct form on the lines below.

What is in store for the future? I think our lifes will change. Maybe humans will have four foots. Then we will be able to run faster. Maybe we will have super-sharp toothes. Then we will use them instead of scissorses. Science will change the world in many ways. Tomato might be bigger than gooses. Mouses might be as strong as mooses. I think the world will be a very strange place!

_____   _____

_____   _____

_____   _____

_____   _____

Writing Activity

Write a personal narrative about something that you think will happen in the future. Use the irregular plural nouns that you learned.

_____

_____

_____

_____

_____

© Macmillan/McGraw-Hill

 At Home: Trade personal narratives with your child. Then proofread each other's work for correct plural nouns.

A. Is the underlined noun singular or plural? Write your answer on the line.

1. There are many <u>deer</u> where we live. _____

2. There used to be <u>salmon</u> in the river. _____

3. I caught a <u>trout</u> last year. _____

4. The <u>mice</u> were very quick. _____

5. The pair of <u>scissors</u> is on the table. _____

6. A <u>buffalo</u> was standing by the lake. _____

7. I saw a group of <u>moose</u> beyond the trees. _____

8. The <u>sheep</u> made a loud noise. _____

B. Write *yes* if the plural form of the underlined noun is correct. Write *no* if it is not correct. Then write the correct plural form.

9. The <u>womans</u> at the museum helped us. _____

10. They showed us pictures of <u>buffalo</u>. _____

11. We learned how <u>fishs</u> live underwater. _____

12. We saw what our <u>lifes</u> may be like in the future. _____

13. We will be the adults, not the <u>children</u>! _____

14. The shapes of the animals' <u>foots</u> are different. _____

15. Several <u>mans</u> were standing around one exhibit. _____

16. We got to see skulls that showed their <u>tooths</u>. _____

17. Smaller objects were on some <u>shelves</u>. _____

18. We saw arrowheads and old <u>knifes</u>. _____

Name_____

- Some nouns have special plural forms.
- A few nouns have the same singular and plural forms.

Mechanics

- Every sentence begins with a capital letter.
- A statement ends with a period.
- A command ends with a period.
- An exclamation ends with an exclamation point.
- A question ends with a question mark.

Rewrite the sentences with the correct plural form of the noun in parentheses. Add capital letters and end marks to each sentence.

1. the dentist is checking my (tooth) next week

_____

2. will I be five (foot) tall next year

_____

3. I will plant (tomato) next summer

_____

4. hand me the (scissors)

_____

5. hey, look at those (sheep)

_____

6. will those (man) leave tonight

_____

© Macmillan/McGraw-Hill

Name _____

> • A **possessive noun** is a noun that shows who or what owns or has something.
> • Add an **apostrophe** (') and an *s* to a singular noun to make it possessive.

Write the possessive form of each underlined noun. The first one is done for you.

1. the rays of the <u>sun</u>   the _____sun's_____ rays

2. the light of the <u>moon</u>   the _____ light

3. the orbit of the <u>Earth</u>   the _____ orbit

4. the planets of the <u>galaxy</u>   the _____ planets

5. rings of <u>Saturn</u>   _____ rings

6. the name of the <u>planet</u>   the _____ name

7. the climate of <u>Jupiter</u>   _____ climate

8. the distance of the <u>star</u>   the _____ distance

 At Home: Take turns with your child saying sentences using these possessive nouns. Have your child write down the correct form of the noun.

The Planets in Our Solar System
Book I/Unit 2

 51

Name_____

> • Add an apostrophe (') to make most plural nouns possessive.
>   Example: planets' names
>
> • Add an apostrophe (') and *s* to form the possessive of plural nouns that do not end in *s*.
>   Example: people's view

Write the possessive form of each underlined noun.

1. the size of the <u>rings</u>   the _____ size

2. the orbits of the <u>planets</u>   the _____ orbits

3. the telescope of the <u>children</u>   the _____ telescope

4. the tails of <u>comets</u>   the _____ tails

5. the distances of the <u>orbits</u>   the _____ distances

6. the lengths of the <u>days</u>   the _____ lengths

7. the speeds of the <u>meteors</u>   the _____ speeds

8. the patterns of the <u>stars</u>   the _____ patterns

9. the lights of the <u>pulsars</u>   the _____ lights

10. the shapes of the <u>moons</u>   the _____ shapes

At Home: Have your child write two sentences using the possessive of a plural noun.

Name

> - Add an apostrophe (') and an *s* to a singular noun to make it possessive.
> - Add an apostrophe (') to make most plural nouns possessive.
> - Add an apostrophe (') and an *s* to form the possessive of plural nouns that do not end in *s*.

Complete each sentence with the possessive form of the noun in parentheses.

1. Both (classes) _____ visits to the science center were on Wednesday.

2. The (students) _____ buses arrived at 9:00 a.m.

3. The classes saw a show about the (Earth) _____ solar system.

4. The (planets) _____ paths around the sun are called orbits.

5. The (orbits) _____ lengths are all different.

6. A (comet) _____ tail is made of dust and gas.

7. The (Science Center) _____ guides talked to the students.

8. The guides answered the (children) _____ questions.

9. The (sun) _____ rays are very powerful.

10. The (universe) _____ size is amazing.

11. A (ring) _____ shape may not be circular.

12. What are those (stars) _____ patterns?

 At Home: Have your child take turns reading the completed sentences aloud.

The Planets in Our Solar System
Book 1/Unit 2

Name_____

> • A possessive noun is a noun that shows who or what owns or has something.

Proofread the radio ad for incorrect possessive nouns. Circle each incorrect possessive noun and write its correct form on the lines below.

How long is Earths orbit   What are Saturns rings made of   how hot is the suns' surface?   Learn all this and more in "Our Super Solar System," a new show at the Museum of Science!

call 555-SOLAR for todays show times.   Mondays shows are sold out.   Ask about our special childrens's shows for schools and other groups   So get in orbit and come out to the Museum of Science!

_____

_____

Writing Activity

Rewrite the radio ad using correct forms of possessive nouns. Make sure every sentence begins with a capital letter and has an end mark.

_____

_____

_____

_____

_____

_____

_____

 At Home: Have your child look at ads in magazines. Ask him or her to make a list of possessive nouns that he or she finds.

Name _____

A. Read each sentence. Find the correct possessive form for the singular noun in parenthesis.

1. A (planet) orbit is its path around the sun.
   - **A.** planet
   - **B.** planet's
   - **C.** planets'
   - **D.** planets's

2. The (sun) rays give heat and light.
   - **A.** sun
   - **B.** suns
   - **C.** sun's
   - **D.** suns'

B. Read each sentence. Find the correct possessive form for the plural noun in parenthesis.

3. The (planets) moons travel with them around the sun.
   - **A.** planets
   - **B.** planets's
   - **C.** planets'
   - **D.** planet

4. The (orbits) paths are not shaped like circles.
   - **A.** orbits
   - **B.** orbits'
   - **C.** orbit's'
   - **D.** orbits's

5. The tower blocked the (people) view of the sky.
   - **A.** peoples
   - **B.** people's
   - **C.** peoples'
   - **D.** people

Name_____

- A **possessive noun** is a noun that shows who or what owns or has something.

Mechanics

- Add an apostrophe (') and an *s* to a singular to make it possessive.
- Add an apostrophe (') to make most plural nouns possessive.
- Add an apostrophe (') and an *s* to form the possessive of plural nouns that do not end in *s*.

Work with a partner. One of you reads the sentences aloud. The other proofreads. Look for the possessive forms of singular nouns and plural nouns. Put in the missing apostrophes. The proofreader reads the corrected sentences aloud.

1. The Earths solar system has nine planets.

_____

2. At the solar systems center is the sun.

_____

3. The planets orbits take them far from the sun.

_____

4. The planets days are all different lengths.

_____

5. The suns rays helps us live on Earth.

_____

Name_____

> • Some nouns are the subjects of sentences. Sometimes two
> subjects can be joined with *and*.
>
> Separate: Teachers help us learn.
>
>   Parents help us learn.
>
> Combined: Teachers and parents help us learn.

Combine the subjects of the sentences. Write the new sentence.

1. Teachers like class trips. Students like class trips.

_____

2. Jim went to see a play. Tess went to see a play.

_____

3. The stories were very good. The songs were very good.

_____

4. The words were written by the play's author. The songs were written by
the play's author.

_____

5. The author talked to us after the play. The actors talked to us after the
play.

_____

6. The students enjoyed the play. The teachers enjoyed the play.

_____

At Home: Have your child make up a sentence. Next, you
say the same sentence with a new subject. Then have your
child write the combined sentences.

Author: A True Story • **Book I/Unit 2**   57

Name _____

> • Two sentences can be combined by joining the nouns in the
>   predicate with *and*.
>   Separate: Teachers help children.
>   Teachers help adults.
>   Combined: Teachers help children and adults.
>   Separate: The book described tigers.
>   The book described lions.
>   Combined: The book described tigers and lions.

**Combine the sentences. Use *and* to join the underlined nouns.
Write the new sentences.**

1. Authors write books. Authors write short stories.

_____

2. Authors imagine places. Authors imagine characters.

_____

3. An author visited Ms. Green's class. An author visited Mr. Finn's class.

_____

4. The author wrote about imaginary people. The author wrote about
real people.

_____

5. The author discussed her books. The author discussed her characters.

_____

6. The author heard our stories. The author heard our poems.

_____

© Macmillan/McGraw-Hill

At Home: Have your child write two endings to this
sentence: *I write _____.* Then have him or her combine
the two sentences.

Name _____

> • The first and main words in a book title are capitalized.
> • Book titles are underlined or italicized.
>   Example: I read life in antarctica.
>   I read <u>Life in Antarctica</u>.

Find the book title in each sentence. Write it correctly.

1. I just read the mystery of the talking cat.

_____

2. My favorite book is return to forest danger.

_____

3. Now I am reading the last house at the corner.

_____

4. Brian is reading the pigs and i.

_____

5. Have you read rainy summer?

_____

6. Our class is reading star in the west.

_____

7. Make sure you read the journey of the black pearl.

_____

8. My brother loves the book the mighty mouse of giant town.

_____

_____

At Home: Take turns saying book titles with your child. Have your child write the title down using correct capitalization and underlining.

Name_____

- Two sentences can be combined by joining two nouns with *and*.
- Some nouns are the subjects of sentences.
- Some nouns are in the predicate.

Proofread the book review. Find two pairs of sentences that can be combined. Then write the new combined sentences on the lines below.

I just finished a book called first year. It is about Nicole. It is about Laurie. They are twins it is their first year at boarding school. the girls had problems School wasn't easy. they wanted to go home. Then Nicole made new friends. Then Laurie made new friends. They had fun.

I couldn't put this book down. I would tell others to read this book.

_____

_____

Writing Activity

Rewrite the book review with the new combined sentences. Make sure all sentences begin with a capital letter and end with an end mark. Make sure that book titles are written correctly.

_____

_____

_____

_____

_____

At Home: Have your child write about a book he or she liked. Have your child use at least two combined sentences in the review.

© Macmillan/McGraw-Hill

Name_____

A. Combine the following sentences using *and*.

1. Our class wrote stories. Our class wrote poems.

_____

2. Rita went to the library. Pete went to the library.

_____

3. Kim described her dog. Kim described her cat.

_____

B. Each pair of sentences can be combined. Write the two nouns that can be joined with the word *and*. Use capital letters correctly.

4. Ann visited the library. Ken visited the library.

_____ and _____

5. Books have words. Books have pictures.

_____ and _____

6. Ann's favorite book describes spiders. Ann's favorite book describes beetles.

_____ and _____

7. The same author studies ants. The same author studies grasshoppers.

_____ and _____

8. Ken looked up insects. Ken looked up bugs.

_____ and _____

9. We checked out books. We checked out magazines.

_____ and _____

Name_____

- Two sentences can be combined by joining two nouns with *and*.
- Sometimes two nouns that are subjects can be joined with *and*.
- Sometimes two nouns in the predicate can be joined with *and*.

Read the sentences. Combine the sentences by joining the underlined words with *and*. Make sure that book titles are written correctly.

1. I read <u>travels with tiger</u>. I read <u>blue skies</u>.

_____

2. travels with tiger describes <u>a boy</u>. travels with tiger describes <u>a tiger</u>.

_____

3. They cross the <u>land</u>. They cross the <u>sea</u>.

_____

4. They see strange <u>people</u>. They see strange <u>places</u>.

_____

5. blue skies portrays <u>Kris</u>. blue skies portrays <u>Tom</u>.

_____

6. <u>Kris</u> starred in a movie. <u>Tom</u> starred in a movie.

_____

7. Now they have <u>a new town</u>. Now they have <u>a new school</u>.

_____

8. They have <u>new friends</u>. They have <u>new teachers</u>.

_____

© Macmillan/McGraw-Hill

Look at the underlined nouns. Put a C over common nouns. Put a P over proper nouns.

Yesterday my class visited (1) Springfield Park. Mr. Johnson showed us where the (2) animals and birds live. We saw a chipmunk gather (3) nuts. We also saw a robin feed its chicks. (4) Mr. Johnson explained that birds eat worms. It was a fun day. Dad says I will visit other (5) parks when we vacation in (6) Arizona.

Write the plural form of each noun in parentheses.

7. I saw many (fish) in the pond. _____

8. The (box) are too heavy to carry. _____

9. Those (baby) like to laugh. _____

10. He baked two (batch) of cookies. _____

11. The (leaf) turn colors in the fall. _____

12. Mike ate two (piece) of toast for breakfast. _____

Write the possessive form of each noun in parentheses.

13. (Rita) sister is in second grade. _____

14. The two (dogs) tails are wagging. _____

15. (Children) books are fun to read. _____

16. The (trees) leaves are falling. _____

17. (Monday) concert starts at noon. _____

18. The (woman) dress is green. _____

Name

**Read the passages. Choose the two nouns that can be joined
with the word *and*. Mark your answer.**

(19) Jena liked to write about all kinds of things. Will liked to write about
all kinds of things. They began to write together. (20) They wrote many
stories. They wrote many plays. They began to print their work. Soon they
had their own magazine.

19. A. Jena and things

  B. Will and things

  C. Jena and Will

  D. Cannot be combined

20. F. stories and plays

  G. They and stories

  H. They and plays

  J. Cannot be combined

(21) I like to read about kids my age. I like to read about unusual places.
I read a book about two friends. Their names were Chris and Sarah.
(22) Chris's family moved to Antarctica. Sarah's family moved to Antarctica.
It was hard to get used to living in a new strange place. They helped each
other learn to live there.

21. A. kids my age and unusual
    places

  B. books and unusual places

  C. books and kids my age

  D. Cannot be combined

22. F. Chris's family and Antarctica

  G. Sarah's family and
    Antarctica

  H. Chris's family and Sarah's
    family

  J. Cannot be combined

Name_____

- An **action verb** is a word that shows action.
- An action verb tells what the subject of the sentence does.
  Carly <u>sings</u> at parties.
  She <u>talks</u> to her friends.

Circle the action verb in each sentence.

1. Carly answers the door.

2. She greets the guests.

3. Everyone works together in the kitchen.

4. Ray slices the tomatoes with a knife.

5. Tracy makes the sandwiches.

6. Brian sets the table.

7. The whole group sits down.

8. Everyone eats lunch.

9. The food tastes good.

10. Carly smiles happily.

At Home: Have your child choose four of the action verbs on this page. Ask him or her to use them to create a short story.

Name_____

- An **action verb** is a word that shows action.
- An action verb tells what the subject of the sentence does.
  Some action verbs tell about actions that are hard to see.
      The soup <u>cooks</u> slowly.
      Jana <u>waits</u> for it.

Circle the action verb in each sentence.

1. Ed watches the chef.

2. He likes TV cooking shows.

3. He listens to the instructions.

4. He learns about cooking.

5. Ed imagines new recipes.

6. Ed plans a dinner.

7. Ed and Dad decide on a menu.

8. Dad shops for food with Ed.

9. The food smells good.

10. Mom, Dad, and Wendy love the dinner.

11. We buy fresh vegetables.

12. Ed and Wendy work together.

13. Dad cuts the food.

14. Ed mixes the food in the bowl.

15. Everyone eats the meal.

 At Home: Have your child make a list of verbs that have to do with cooking.

Name

> • Use a comma between the name of a city or town and a state.
> • Use a comma between the names of a street address, a town, and a state.
> • Use a comma between the day and the year in a date.

Add commas in the correct places.

1. The big family party is on June 6 2006.

_____

2. We are driving to Columbus Ohio.

_____

3. We will visit Philadelphia Pennsylvania.

_____

4. I hope to see my cousins from Tampa Florida.

_____

5. We haven't seen them since June 30 2003.

_____

6. That party was in Boston Massachusetts.

_____

7. Mom's cake recipe for the party comes from San Francisco California.

_____

_____

8. The recipe is from a newspaper dated December 15 1984.

_____

_____

© Macmillan/McGraw-Hill

At Home: Have your child write three dates and state names. Ask him or her to use them in a sentence.

Name _____

Proofread the story. Start by finding and circling the action verbs.

I like the day after thanksgiving. The same thing happens on this day every year. Grandma gets up early goes to the kitchen and cooks. She takes the leftovers and uses them for soup. She carves the turkey cuts the vegetables and heats the water. Later we have a delicious meal. George loves grandma's soup. He always has two bowls. He also eats plenty of cranberries stuffing and pie. Everybody enjoys this special day.

Rewrite the story. Make sure commas are used correctly. Put in capital letters where they are needed.

_____

_____

_____

_____

_____

_____

_____

_____

_____

At Home: Have your child write a journal entry that tells about a special day. Then have your child circle the action verbs.

Name_____

A. Read each sentence. Find the action verb in the sentence and write it on the line.

1. The chef wakes up early. _____

2. She shops at the market. _____

3. She opens the restaurant. _____

4. She bakes loaves of bread. _____

5. She slices pieces of fruit. _____

6. The chef creates menus. _____

7. She tastes some samples. _____

8. She sprinkles on the spices. _____

B. Circle the action verb that best fits each sentence.

> eats   takes   cooks   looks   orders   toasts   cleans

9. A customer (looks, decides, egg) at the menu.

10. He (cleans, orders, menu) breakfast.

11. The chef (lays, cooks, sings) the eggs.

12. She (creates, chops, toasts) the bread.

13. The waiter (makes, takes, buys) the food to the table.

14. He (eats, cleans, looks) the food.

15. The waiter (wakes, cleans, builds) the table.

Name_____

- An **action verb** is a word that shows action.
- Some action verbs tell about actions that are hard to see.
   She <u>listens</u> carefully.
   The kitchen <u>smells</u> good.

Draw a line from each sentence to the picture of the action it tells about. Underline the action verb in each sentence.

1. Jay sips the drink.

2. Karen peels the orange.

3. Garth pours the water.

4. The pie cools off.

5. Ann opens the jar.

© Macmillan/McGraw-Hill

Name _____

> - A verb in the **present tense** tells what happens now.
> - A present-tense verb must **agree** with its subject.
> - Add -s to most verbs if the subject is singular.
> - Do not add -s or -es to a present-tense verb when the subject is plural or *I* or *you*.

Each sentence is followed by two forms of a verb. Choose the form of the verb that correctly agrees with the subject of the sentence. Circle your answer.

1. Andy _____ to do a show.   want   wants

2. He _____ some tricks.   learn   learns

3. Lisa _____ him write jokes and riddles.   help   helps

4. I _____ to ask the audience to answer the riddles.   plan   plans

5. The girl _____ plenty of clues in the riddles.   put   puts

6. You _____ to the show.   come   comes

7. I _____ at the jokes.   laugh   laughs

8. You _____ the riddle.   solve   solves

9. I _____ some popcorn.   share   shares

10. Andy _____ to the crowd.   bow   bows

© Macmillan/McGraw-Hill

At Home: Have your child write two sentences, one using a verb with a singular subject and one using a verb with a plural subject.

Name_____

- A verb in the **present tense** tells what happens now.
- A present-tense verb must **agree** with its subject.
- Add -*s* to most verbs if the subject is singular.
- Add -*es* to verbs that end in *s, ch, sh, x,* or *z* if the subject is singular.
- Change *y* to *i* and add -*es* to verbs that end with a consonant and *y.*
- Do not add -*s* or -*es* to a present-tense verb when the subject is plural or *I* or *you.*

| She <u>wishes</u>. | The ink <u>dries</u>. |
| They <u>wish</u>. | The papers <u>dry</u>. |

For each verb below, write the form that agrees with the subject given.

1. carry   Ann _____.

2. pitch   Mike _____.

3. wash   I _____.

4. fix   You _____.

5. guess   Flora _____.

6. push   You _____.

7. match   I _____.

8. mix   Kim _____.

9. squash   She _____.

10. fly   Don _____.

11. snatch   You _____.

12. toss   Lee _____.

At Home: Have your child use three verbs from this page in sentences.

Name_____

- A verb in the **present tense** tells what happens now.
- A present-tense verb must **agree** with its subject.
- Add -s to most verbs if the subject is singular.
- Add -es to verbs that end in s, ch, sh, x, or z if the subject is singular.
- Change y to i and add -es to verbs that end with a consonant and y.
- Do not add -s or -es to a present-tense verb when the subject is plural or I or you.

Underline the correct verb in each sentence below.

1. Fourteen guests (come, comes) to Sarah's party.

2. They (listen, listens) to riddles.

3. The riddles (give, gives) clues.

4. The clues (lead, leads) to prizes.

5. Some guests (search, searches) in the house.

6. Others (look, looks) outside the house.

7. Sarah (worry, worries) that the riddles are too hard.

8. The guests (laugh, laughs) as they follow the funny clues.

9. Soon they (find, finds) their prizes.

10. "I hope you (enjoy, enjoys) your prizes!" says Sarah.

11. A girl (pick, picks) up a clue.

12. Everyone (sit, sits) at the table.

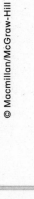

At Home: Work with your child to write a present-tense story using at least one verb each that ends in s, ch, sh, x, z, and a consonant followed by y.

Name_____

Proofread the paragraph. Circle any verbs that do not agree with their subjects.

Dad tell us riddles when we go on car trips. The riddles makes the ride more fun. They sounds easy at first. There is always a trick, though. He ask how many letters are in the alphabet. We tell him twenty-six. Then Dad laugh at us. He say, "Count again. There are only eleven letters in the word alphabet." When we complains, Dad gives us a hint. "Think first," he explains. Sometimes Kris hurry up with her answer. He ask, "Are you sure?" When I rushes my guess, he tells me, "Listen again." Now we makes better guesses. Sometimes we even gets them right!

Rewrite the paragraph. Write the verbs so that they agree with their subjects.

_____

_____

_____

_____

_____

_____

_____

_____

_____

_____

_____

_____

 At Home: Take turns making up riddles with your child. Then check each other's work for subject-verb agreement.

Name _____

A. Choose the correct form of each of the following verbs to go with the singular subject in the sentence below.

The Princess _____.

1. A. guess

   B. guesses

   C. guessies

   D. gesses

2. A. worrys

   B. worryes

   C. worris

   D. worries

You _____.

3. A. wishes

   B. wish

   C. wishs

   D. wishies

4. A. thinkes

   B. think

   C. thinks

   D. thinkses

B. Decide if the subject of each sentence is singular or plural. Then choose the correct verb to agree with the subject. Mark your answer.

5. The Princess _____ a riddle.

   A. invent

   B. invents

6. Her friends _____ for clues.

   A. search

   B. searches

7. I _____ the answer.

   A. hide

   B. hides

8. Everyone _____ the riddle is hard.

   A. say

   B. says

© Macmillan/McGraw-Hill

Name_____

- A verb in the **present tense** tells what happens now.
- A present-tense verb must **agree** with its subject.
- Add -*s* to most verbs if the subject is singular.
- Add -*es* to verbs that end in *s, ch, sh, x,* or *z* if the subject is singular.
- Change *y* to *i* and add -*es* to verbs that end with a consonant and *y*.
- Do not add -*s* or -*es* to a present-tense verb when the subject is plural or *I* or *you*.

    She wishes.   The ink dries.
    They wish.   The papers dry.

Work with a partner. One can read each sentence aloud while the other writes down and corrects the verb in the sentence. The verbs are underlined.

1. Tom create a riddle for his friends. _____

2. They asks him for hints. _____

3. You tries to help them. _____

4. Steve mix up the clues. _____

5. Kate guess wrong. _____

6. Mark wish he knew the answer. _____

7. We makes a guess. _____

8. She watch Tom's face. _____

9. I says she is correct. _____

10. Everyone cheer for Lola. _____

Name_____

> • A verb in the **past-tense** tells about an action that already happened.
> • Add *-ed* to most verbs to show past tense.
>   We <u>walked</u> to the beach.

Find the past-tense verb in each sentence. Write it on the line.

1. We placed our towels on the sand. _____

2. Mom stretched out on her towel. _____

3. We picked up our buckets. _____

4. I filled mine with sand. _____

5. Rob stacked the buckets of sand. _____.

6. They formed towers at each corner. _____

7. In the center, I shaped a big square of sand. _____

8. I carved windows into the square. _____

9. We smoothed out the edges. _____

10. Everyone liked the size of our castle. _____

11. We marked some spots in the sand. _____

12. I wiped off my sneakers. _____

13. Rob poured some water. _____

14. We fixed a loose spot. _____

15. We played for many hours. _____

At Home: Have your child make lists of verbs. Have him or her take turns using the past-tense forms of the verbs in sentences.

Name_____

- A verb in the **past-tense** tells about an action that already happened.
- Add -*ed* to most verbs to show past tense.
- If a verb ends with *e*, drop the *e* and add -*ed* to show past tense.
- If a verb ends with a consonant and *y*, change *y* to *i* and add -*ed*.
- If a verb ends with one vowel and one consonant, double the consonant and add -*ed*.

Choose the correct past-tense verb for each sentence. Circle your answer.

1. Felix _____ across the beach. marchedd   marched

2. The hot sand _____ his feet. burnd   burned

3. The sand dunes _____ towards the water. sloped   slopped

4. Felix _____ down the dunes. rolld   rolled

5. He _____ the sand off his face. dusted   dustted

6. Casey _____ from the water. wavved   waved

7. Felix _____ towards the water. skippd   skipped

8. The waves _____ over his feet. splashd   splashed

9. Felix _____ on his back. floated   floatted

10. Casey _____ to do a handstand. tryed   tried

11. Jellyfish _____ on the water. coasted   coastted

12. We _____ under the shade. ressted   rested

 At Home: Have your child write three sentences about a trip to the beach. Have him or her use past-tense verbs.

Name_____

> • Use **commas** to separate three or more words in a series.
>   The stone hopped, skipped, and splashed across the water.

Correct the sentences by changing the underlined verbs to the past tense. Add a comma after words in a series. Write the new sentence on the line.

1. The bird flap its wings coast through the air and turn towards shore.

_____

_____

2. He drift through the sky slow down and land on a rock.

_____

_____

3. The bird jump to another rock pick up a piece of bread and swallow it.

_____

_____

4. The bird find a candy wrapper a pretzel and a few bugs.

_____

_____

5. He poke pull and rip apart the wrapper.

_____

6. Then the bird fly into the clear bright blue sky.

_____

At Home: Have your child make up three sentences using a series each of nouns, verbs, and adjectives.

Name_____

> - A verb in the **past-tense** tells about an action that already happened.
> - Add *-ed* to most verbs to show past tense.
> - If a verb ends with *e*, drop the *e* and add *-ed* to show past tense.
> - If a verb ends with a consonant and *y*, change *y* to *i* and add *-ed*.
> - If a verb ends with one vowel and one consonant, double the consonant and add *-ed*.

Proofread the paragraph. Circle any past-tense verbs that are incorrect.

On Saturday, our class clean up the beach at Perch Bay. We picked up litter twigs and seaweed. We packked the other garbage into bags. We discoverred all kinds of things while we work. Sam showd me movie tickets bottle tops and even a watch. The beach lookked much better when we were finished. The sand glitterd like the sun on the water. I'm glad we workd so hard at the beach.

Rewrite the paragraph. Write the past-tense verbs correctly. Add commas where necessary.

_____

_____

_____

_____

_____

_____

_____

_____

 At Home: Have your child proofread his or her rewritten paragraph.

Name_____

A. Read each sentence. Circle the past-tense verbs. Rewrite each sentence to add any commas that are missing.

1. The raindrops bounced off the rocks shells and sand.

   _____

2. The storm raced across the ocean dunes and beach.

   _____

3. The sky clouds and sand turned a darker color.

   _____

4. The wind and rain damaged the boats rafts and docks in the water.

   _____

   _____

5. The lifeguards sailors swimmers and I left the water.

   _____

6. Mist rolled over the town its beaches and my favorite dunes.

   _____

   _____

B. Give the past-tense form of each action verb in parentheses. Write the answer on the line.

7. The sun (dry) off the sand. _____

8. Clumps of seaweed (wash) onto the shore. _____

9. Seagulls (carry) away bits of food. _____

10. Crabs (crawl) out of their holes. _____

11. Stray twigs (skip) across the water. _____

12. Tiny birds (scurry) away from the waves. _____

© Macmillan/McGraw-Hill

Name_____

- A verb in the **past-tense** tells about an action that already happened.
- Add -*ed* to most verbs to show past tense.
- If a verb ends with *e*, drop the *e* and add -*ed* to show past tense.
- If a verb ends with a consonant and *y*, change *y* to *i* and add -*ed*.
- If a verb ends with one vowel and one consonant, double the consonant and add -*ed*.

Look at the picture. Then read the paragraph that tells what happened. Rewrite the paragraph. Write the past-tense verbs correctly.

    We plaied on the beach. Tara punchd the ball. The ball poppedd over the net. Jess knock it back. Will tryed to catch the ball. It droped into the sand.

_____

_____

_____

Now write two or three sentences about the rest of the game. Use past-tense verbs.

_____

_____

_____

Name_____

- A **present-tense verb** tells what happens now.
- A **past-tense verb** tells about an action that already happened.
- A verb in the **future-tense** tells about an action that is going to happen.
- To write about the future, use the special verb *will*.

Each sentence below has a time clue that tells if the action is happening now, in the past, or in the future. Choose the correct form of the verb to complete each sentence. Write your answer on the line.

1. Now Pete (needs, needed) a gift for his Uncle Carl. _____

2. Tomorrow he (will shop, shop) for something. _____

3. Years ago, Uncle Carl (will play, played) baseball. _____

4. Today he (works, worked) as an announcer at games.

   _____

5. Now Pete (walks, walked) through the stores. _____

6. In the past, his mother (will pick, picked) out presents for him.

   _____

7. Now he (chooses, will choose) a big book about baseball.

   _____

8. The baseball stars in the book (play, played) many years ago.

   _____

9. Pete (will give, gives) it to Uncle Carl on Saturday. _____

10. Uncle Carl (enjoyed, will enjoy) reading the book on the plane ride

    home. _____

At Home: Ask your child to write three past-tense and three present-tense sentences about a visit from a relative.

Name _____

- A **present-tense verb** tells what happens now.
- A **past-tense verb** tells about an action that already happened.
- A **future-tense verb** tells about an action that is going to happen.
- To write about the future, use the special verb <u>will</u>.

Circle the verb in each sentence. Decide whether it is in the present tense or the past tense. Write *present* or *past* on the line after the sentence. On the line below, rewrite the sentence in the future tense.

1. Leah sits by the window. _____

   _____

2. Mira listens for the sound of the car. _____

   _____

3. Mom waited at the airport. _____

   _____

4. She looked at the crowds. _____

   _____

5. Mira wonders about the surprise. _____

   _____

6. Leah thinks about the surprise, too. _____

   _____

7. Mira suggests a new job for Mom. _____

   _____

8. Mom spotted a familiar face. _____

   _____

 At Home: Have your child write three sentences about things he or she plans to do next weekend. Tell your child to use future-tense verbs.

Name_____

• Use **quotation marks** at the beginning and end of a speaker's exact words.

"Let's go!" called Dad.

"I'm right behind you," said Robert.

Rewrite each sentence. Add quotation marks at the beginning and end of the speaker's exact words.

1. Let's go buy a gift for Mom, said Dad.

_____

2. What should we get her? Adam wondered.

_____

3. Do you have any ideas? asked Ali.

_____

4. Don't you think she would like candy? suggested Rob.

_____

_____

5. You just want a big box of candy! yelled Adam.

_____

6. What's wrong with that? asked Rob.

_____

7. Please be serious! said Ali.

_____

8. Do you think she'd like a bracelet? asked Rob.

_____

At Home: Take turns writing lines of dialogue. Write a line without any quotation marks or commas before names. Then have your child fill in the quotation marks and commas.

Name_____

> - A **present-tense verb** tells what happens now.
> - A **past-tense verb** tells about an action that already happened.
> - A **future-tense verb** tells about an action that is going to happen.

Proofread these lines of dialogue. Circle any verbs that are not written in the correct tense.

"I hopped you can help me, said Jim.

I will tries my best, said Ann.

I needs a gift for Aunt Cara, said Jim.

She will mention something last week, said Ann.

Tell me what! cry Jim.

She said that next year she will learned to fly, said Ann.

"I will looked for a book about airplanes, said Jim.

"That's great! I think she will liked that," said Ann.

Rewrite the dialogue. Write verbs correctly. Make sure that quotation marks are in the right place.

_____

_____

_____

_____

_____

_____

 At Home: Write a dialogue about past events. Then, have your child rewrite it in future-tense.

A. Choose the correct verb tense for each of the following sentences. Circle and write your answer.

1. Next week we _____ to our aunt's house.

   A. travels   B. travel   C. will travel   D. traveled

2. She _____ us last year.

   A. visits   B. visit   C. will visit   D. visited

3. Mom is here and _____ that we buy a gift for Aunt Lily.

   A. suggests   B. suggest   C. will suggest   D. suggested

4. Later today we _____ for a gift.

   A. shops   B. shop   C. will shop   D. shopped

B. Decide if the verb in each sentence should be past-tense, present-tense, or future-tense. Find the verb that correctly completes the sentence. Circle and write your answer.

5. Laurie _____ to buy a gift for her sister right now.

   A. needs   B. need   C. will need   D. needed

6. Tomorrow I _____ her find something.

   A. helps   B. help   C. will help   D. helped

7. Long ago, I _____ shopping.

   A. hates   B. hate   C. will hate   D. hated

8. Now I _____ looking for the perfect gift.

   A. likes   B. like   C. will like   D. liked

- A **present-tense verb** tells what happens now.
- A **past-tense verb** tells about an action that already happened.
- A **future-tense verb** tells about an action that is going to happen.

Work with a partner to correct the sentences below. Each sentence has a verb that is in the wrong tense. As one partner reads each sentence aloud, the other listens to the time clue in the sentence. Then both will decide what tense to use. Rewrite each sentence correctly.

1. The stores opened a half hour from now.

_____

2. We wait here for thirty minutes until opening time.

_____

3. Right now we needed to find a gift quickly.

_____

4. At this minute, I will think that Aunt Carol would like a scarf .

_____

5. Last year we paint a plate for her.

_____

6. We will use her favorite colors on the plate back then.

_____

7. Right now we rushed inside the store.

_____

8. Next year we started earlier.

_____

Name _____

> • Two sentences with the same subject can be combined by joining the predicates with *and*.
>
> Two sentences: The birds hop. The birds flutter.
> Combined sentence: The birds hop and flutter.

The pairs of sentences below share the same subject. Make them into one sentence by using the word *and* to join the predicates. Write the new sentence on the line.

1. The painting glows. The painting shimmers.

   _____

2. The artist waits. The artist watches.

   _____

3. The people point. The people whisper.

   _____

4. Each painting is beautiful. Each painting is exciting.

   _____

5. The paintings surprise. The paintings amaze.

   _____

6. The figures jump. The figures dance.

   _____

7. The frames are large. The frames are gold

   _____

8. The colors shine. The colors glitter.

   _____

9. The crowd buzzes. The crowd chatters.

   _____

At Home: Make up a short sentence. Have your child use the same subject to make another sentence. Then ask him or her to combine the sentences.

Name_____

> • Two sentences with the same subject can be combined by joining
> the predicates with *and*.
>
> Two sentences: Jan draws with pencils.
>   Jan sculpts with clay.
>
> Combined sentence: Jan draws with pencils and sculpts
>   with clay.

**Underline the predicate in each pair of sentences. Then combine
the two sentences and write your one sentence on the line.**

1. Elaine goes to art school. Elaine studies painting.

_____

2. The students sketch outside. The students paint in the classroom.

_____

3. Elaine mixes paint. Elaine invents colors.

_____

4. The brush sweeps the canvas. The brush leaves colors behind.

_____

5. The students look at paintings. The students talk about them.

_____

6. Elaine stands near the tree. Elaine draws the bird.

_____

7. The teacher points to a painting. The teacher explains it.

_____

8. Elaine finishes her painting. Elaine shows it to others.

_____

© Macmillan/McGraw-Hill

At Home: Have your child write pairs of sentences with the
same subject. Then have your child combine the sentences
using *and*.

Name_____

> • Two sentences with the same subject can be combined by joining the predicates with *and*.
> • Use a comma to separate three or more words in a series.
> • Use a comma between the names of a street address, a city, and a state.
> • Use a comma between the day and the year in a date.

Rewrite each sentence. Add commas in the correct places. Combine sentences that share the same subject.

1. Meg likes movies. Meg reads books.

_____

2. Michael eats corn beets and carrots.

_____

3. I saw Jimmy on June 18 2006.

_____

4. He invited Alvaro Peter Bob and Jose.

_____

5. Hannah saw tigers. Hanna heard lions.

_____

6. Theresa lives in Boston Massachusetts.

_____

7. Joseph has a cat. Joseph wants a dog.

_____

8. Molly lives at 2 Main Street Akron Ohio.

_____

© Macmillan/McGraw-Hill

At Home: Create a play scene with your child that has to do with time. Then, have your child proofread the scene for correct colons.

What Do Illustrators Do? **91**

Book I/Unit 3

Name_____

Proofread the paragraph. Find and underline the pairs of sentences that share the same subject and can be combined.

My mom is an illustrator. She draws pictures for books. She paints pictures for books. I like to watch her work. She reads the book. She takes notes. Sometimes I read it, too. We talk about the characters. We think about how they look. Then Mom makes some sketches. She experiments. She tests out ideas. She decides what belongs on each page. Then she is ready to paint.

Mom decides on colors. Mom mixes the paint. Then she stands at her easel. We talk while she paints. Her brush moves fast. Her brush fills the canvas with color. The shapes grow. The shapes turn into a picture. The finished picture is beautiful.

Rewrite the paragraph with the combined sentences. Make sure colons are used in times.

_____

_____

_____

_____

_____

_____

_____

_____

_____

_____

At Home: Help your child write a scene from a play. Use pairs of sentences that share a subject. Then, have your child rewrite them with combined sentences.

Name_____

A. Each pair of sentences below shares a subject. On the line, write the subject and the predicate of the first sentence. Then write the word *and* followed by the predicate of the second sentence.

1. The artist watches. The artist waits.

   _____

2. The dog stretches. The dog yawns.

   _____

3. The artist chooses colors. The artist mixes them.

   _____

4. The dog wags its tail. The dog poses for the artist.

   _____

B. Join the sentence pairs below into single sentences. Write your answers.

5. Tom picks up the pencil. Tom starts his sketch.

   _____

6. His pencil makes shapes. His pencil sketches lines.

   _____

7. Tom takes out crayons. Tom colors in the drawing.

   _____

8. Randy looks at the picture. Randy praises its bright colors.

   _____

9. Mom finds a frame. Mom puts the picture in it.

   _____

10. Tom takes the picture. Tom hangs it on the wall.

   _____

Name _____

> • Two sentences with the same subject can be combined by joining the predicates with *and*.

Look at the picture. The paragraph that follows describes what the boy and girl in the picture are doing. Revise the paragraph by combining sentences. Join the predicates using the word *and*.

   Martin and Lisa draw pictures. Martin and Lisa write stories. Lisa thinks of a story. Lisa tells it to Martin. He sketches with a pencil. He colors with markers. Lisa adds words. Lisa makes the characters speak. They put the pages together. They create a book. Their friends read the book. Their friends ask for more.

_____

_____

_____

_____

_____

_____

Name_____

Read the passage and pay attention to the tense of the verbs. Then look at the underlined parts. Is there a better way to say each part? If there is, which is the better way? Mark your answer.

(1) The snow. Wind blows it across the street. (2) We runs outside. I try to catch snowflakes. They melt before I can see them up close.

1. A. The snow quietly!
   B. The snow falls quietly.
   C. The snow fall quietly.
   D. No mistake.

2. E. We ran outside.
   F. We runs outside.
   G. We run outside.
   H. No mistake.

Ruth and I picked up shovels. (3) We plow a path in the snow. It sloped down the hill. Ruth got a bucket of water. (4) She poured it on the snow. The snow turned to ice. We slid down the hill over and over. It was a fun afternoon!

3. A. We plowing a path in the snow.
   B. We plowed a path in the snow.
   C. We plows a path in the snow.
   D. No mistake.

4. E. She pour it on the snow.
   F. She pours it on the snow.
   G. She pouring it on the snow.
   H. No mistake.

(5) Last week, I start a big new painting. It showed a busy city park. By the end of class, I had only sketched an outline. (6) Today, I starts to paint. Next week I will finish the whole thing.

5. **A.** Last week, I started a big new painting.
   B. Last week, I will start a big new painting.
   C. Last week, I starts a big new painting.
   D. No mistake

6. **E.** Today, I was starting to paint.
   F. Today, I will start to paint.
   G. Today, I start to paint.
   H. No mistake

Read the passages. Combine the two underlined predicates with the word *and*. Mark the best answer.

(7) Last week, we went on vacation. We camped near the beach. We swam every day. (8) We played volleyball on the beach. We built sandcastles on the beach. It rained one day. We went to the movies. It still was a fun day.

7. **A.** Last week. We went on vacation, we camped near the beach.
   B. Last week, we went on vacation near the beach.
   C. Last week, we went on vacation and camped near the beach.
   D. No mistake.

8. **E.** We played volleyball on the beach, and we built sandcastles on the beach.
   F. We played volleyball and built sandcastles on the beach.
   G. We volleyball and sandcastles on the beach.
   H. No mistake.

© Macmillan/McGraw-Hill

Name_____

- The verbs *be, do,* and *have* all have special forms in the present tense. The chart shows which form to use with a sentence subject.

SUBJECT	BE	DO	HAVE
I	am	do	have
he, she, it	is	does	has
we, you, they	are	do	have

Write the correct present-tense form of *be* to finish each sentence.

1. She _____ our favorite baker.

2. We _____ big fans of her strawberry pie.

3. They _____ the best pies in the world.

4. I _____ certain you will like them.

5. You _____ never hungry when you leave this bakery.

Write the correct present-tense form of *do* to finish each sentence.

6. It _____ take a lot of work to pick strawberries.

7. We _____ think the effort is worth it.

8. He _____ not like strawberries.

9. I can tell that you _____ like them.

10. I _____ think I could eat strawberries every day.

Write the correct present-tense form of *have* to finish each sentence.

11. We _____ many strawberry plants in our garden.

12. You _____ to help me pick the strawberries tomorrow.

13. It _____ to be finished by noon.

14. I _____ a feeling you will like our strawberries.

15. They _____ the most delicious flavor.

At Home: Have your child change the subjects in the sentences on this page from singular to plural (or vice versa) using the correct form of *be, do,* or *have.*

Cook-a-Doodle-Doo! • **Book 2/Unit 4** 97

Name_____

- The verbs *be, do,* and *have* all have special forms in the past tense. The chart shows which form to use with a sentence subject.

SUBJECT	BE	DO	HAVE
I, he, she, it	was	did	had
we, you, they	were	did	had

Write the correct past-tense form of *be* to finish each sentence.

1. She _____ young when she opened the bakery.

2. We _____ her first customers.

3. I _____ happy her pies were so good.

4. They _____ a big success.

5. You _____ not living here at the time.

Write the correct past-tense form of *do* to finish each sentence.

6. Last week we _____ a report on strawberry farming.

7. It _____ make me hungry to talk about my favorite fruit.

8. Fortunately, I _____ bring some strawberries to class.

9. You _____ not eat any.

10. We _____ think you would like them.

Write the correct past-tense form of *have* to finish each sentence.

11. Yesterday we _____ to water the plants in our garden.

12. I _____ a lot of work to do.

13. You _____ to study for your test.

14. My brother and sister said they _____ something else to do.

15. They _____ to clean their rooms so I watered the garden myself.

© Macmillan/McGraw-Hill

At Home: Have your child write a description of his or her friends using different forms of the verbs *be, do,* and *have.*

Name_____

> • Remember that the verbs *be*, *do*, and *have* have special forms. The present-tense forms of *be, do,* and *have* must agree with their subjects. The past-tense form of *be* must agree with its subjects.

Write the correct form of the given verb to finish each sentence.

1. have "I _____ the same food all the time," thought Rooster.

2. have Suddenly, Rooster _____ a great idea.

3. have "Grandmother _____ a great strawberry shortcake recipe in her book," Rooster said.

4. be "I _____ going to make that cake!" announced Rooster.

5. be Rooster _____ very excited about his plan.

6. be Turtle, Iguana, and Pig _____ eager to help Rooster.

7. be "We _____ a team!" said Rooster.

8. do "I'll _____ the reading," said Turtle.

9. do Iguana _____ not know what kind of flour to put in a cake.

10. do Now the recipe _____ not seem as easy as it looked.

11. have "We _____ to read the recipe carefully," Turtle said.

12. be Pig _____ a good mixer.

At Home: Have your child and a family member take turns giving each other subjects in the past or present. Have your child use those subjects to form sentences with the correct form of *have, do,* or *be.*

Cook-a-Doodle-Doo! • **Book 2/Unit 4** 99

Name_____

> • Remember that the verbs *have, do,* and *be* have special forms.

Proofread the passage. Circle any incorrect uses of *have, do,* or *be*.

I is learning to bake. Grandma are teaching me. We was at her house today. She asked if I knew how to bake a strawberry shortcake. I told her I did not. I does like strawberries, though! Grandma agreed to let me help her.

After we baked the cakes we served it to the family.

"I is very impressed," declared Mom.

"It be a fantastic strawberry shortcake!" said Dad.

"You does a great job!" said Grandma.

"We was a good team," I said.

Writing Activity

Rewrite the passage. Use the correct forms of *have, do,* or *be*.

_____

_____

_____

_____

_____

_____

_____

_____

_____

At Home: Have your child look through magazines and find sentences that use *have, do,* or *be.* Have your child read the sentences aloud and match the verbs with their subjects.

Name_____

Choose the correct word to complete each sentence.

1. This story _____ about a rooster who bakes.
  a. are
  b. is
  c. have
  d. am

2. Rooster _____ tired of his regular food.
  a. were
  b. was
  c. am
  d. have

3. He _____ a recipe for strawberry shortcake.
  a. am
  b. is
  c. had
  d. have

4. His friends _____ asked to help.
  a. has
  b. are
  c. is
  d. were

5. They _____ no experience baking!
  a. were
  b. are
  c. has
  d. had

6. They _____ not know what to do in the kitchen.
  a. am
  b. did
  c. had
  d. have

7. The story _____ very entertaining.
  a. is
  b. are
  c. be
  d. has

8. The animals _____ funny things on every page.
  a. was
  b. were
  c. do
  d. does

Name_____

- Remember that the verbs *be, do,* and *have* have special forms.

Mechanics

- Use a comma between the names of a city and a state.
- Use a comma between the day and year in a date.

As you read the paragraph, look for mistakes with the verbs *be, do,* and *have*. Rewrite the paragraph on the lines below. Correct any comma errors you find.

    I have a great time last summer visiting my cousins in Chicago Illinois. Every year I does many fun things with my favorite cousin Gina. She has art lessons every day and do nice drawings. I want to be as good as she are! My Aunt Joan and Uncle John has a garden. We spend a lot of time with them planting seeds. I always has to go home before the flowers bloom. I will see them again on June 30 2007. They is planning to come to our house. I really does like my cousins. They am so much fun!

_____

_____

_____

_____

_____

_____

_____

© Macmillan/McGraw-Hill

Name_____

> • A **linking verb** does not show action. It connects the subject to a noun or adjective in the predicate.
> • The word *be* is a common linking verb. *Be* has special forms in the present tense.
>> I *am* part of a big family.
>> The house *is* big and roomy.
>> All my brothers *are* here.

Write *am, is,* or, *are* to finish each sentence.

1. I _____ on vacation with my family.

2. My brothers and I _____ at a park with lots of rides.

3. The rides _____ fast and scary.

4. But every ride _____ fun.

5. Sam and I _____ happy to stay in the water park.

6. Chris _____ ready to try the roller-coaster.

7. Mom and Dad _____ ready for lunch.

8. Fortunately, my cousins _____ here.

9. I _____ happy to see them.

10. We _____ eager to play together.

11. Mom and Dad _____ glad to be at the park.

12. Sam and Chris _____ at the ice cream stand.

13. I _____ hungry.

14. George _____ on the steps to the ticket booth.

15. My cousin and I _____ near the miniature golf course.

At Home: Have your child write sentences that use each present tense form of *be*.

Name_____

- The verb *be* is a common **linking verb**. *Be* has special forms in the past tense.

    Jim *was* at the door.
    My brothers and I *were* sorry.

For each sentence below, write the verb form of *be* that agrees with the subject of the sentence.

1. My brothers and I _____ always fighting.

2. Dad _____ upset about our fights.

3. The solution _____ to make us work together.

4. Our task _____ to build a tree house.

5. We all _____ eager to have a tree house.

6. I _____ in charge of measuring.

7. Dad _____ there to help us cut and nail.

8. We _____ hard at work.

9. It _____ all very peaceful.

10. We _____ glad we did something together.

11. My brothers and I _____ careful with the nails.

12. The wooden planks _____ everywhere.

13. We _____ out back all day.

14. Dad _____ happy with our progress.

15. We _____ thirsty in the hot sun.

 At Home: Have your child write four sentences about things he or she did yesterday using both *was* and *were*.

- A **sentence** is a group of words that tells a complete thought. A sentence begins with a capital letter.
- A **statement** is a sentence that tells something. It ends with a period.
- A **question** is a sentence that asks something. It ends with a question mark.
- A **command** is a sentence that tells or asks someone to do something. It ends with a period.
- An **exclamation** shows strong feeling. It ends with an exclamation point.

Rewrite the sentences with correct end punctuation and capitalization.

1. there are seven principles of Kwanzaa

_____

2. can you name them all

_____

3. work together

_____

4. we will share each other's problems and responsibilities

_____

5. i can speak for myself

_____

6. wow, that's beautiful

_____

7. what kind of business should we start

_____

 At Home: Have your child write sentences without end marks. Then have him or her ask a family member to put in the correct end marks.

Seven Spools of Thread
Book 2/Unit 4

Name_____

- The verb *be* connects the subject to the rest of the sentence. *Be* has special forms in the present tense and the past tense.

PRESENT	PAST
I *am*	I *was*
The boy *is*	The girl *was*
The boys *are*	The girls *were*

Proofread the story. Circle any linking verbs that are not correct.

my brother and I helped Grandma decorate. She were having a party. I is the oldest, so I got the cake and presents. I arranged them in the center of the table

"That be my job" Carl said. "I did it last year."

Then we started yelling at each other

"Boys" said Grandma. "why don't you work together to arrange the plates and silverware"

So we did and made the table look nice. It are not so bad. in fact, we be a pretty good team

Rewrite the paragraph. Use the correct linking verbs. Make sure that all sentences begin with a capital letter and have an end mark.

_____

_____

_____

_____

_____

_____

 At Home: Have a family member proofread your child's work.

Name

Write the linking verb in each sentence.

1. Kwanzaa is an annual celebration. _____

2. The seven principles of Kwanzaa are very important. _____

3. They are part of African culture. _____

4. We were part of a Kwanzaa celebration at school. _____

5. I was the person in charge of decorations. _____

6. The colors red, black, and green are important. _____

7. What is the best way to hang these pictures? _____

8. Our teacher was happy with our work. _____

Choose a verb from the box to complete each sentence. Some words may be used more than once.

am	is	are	was	were

9. My brothers and I _____ always fighting.

10. I _____ the youngest.

11. Last night, Mom and Dad _____ home early.

12. We _____ all working on a model airplane.

13. It _____ surprisingly easy to work together!

14. Making things _____ not so hard.

15. Mom and Dad _____ proud of us.

Name_____

- The verb *be* connects the subject to the rest of the sentence. *Be* has special forms in the present tense and the past tense.

PRESENT	PAST
I *am*	I *was*
The boy *is*	The girl *was*
The boys *are*	The girls *were*

Read each sentence aloud. Correct the linking verb. Write the sentence with correct capitalization and end marks.

1. this book am <u>Seven Spools of Thread</u>

_____

2. it are the story of seven brothers

_____

3. wow, they was always upset with each other

_____

4. the book am interesting

_____

5. in the past the brothers is selfish

_____

6. the Chief are a wise man and gives good advice

_____

7. the brothers is happy to make peace with each other

_____

8. their cloth were a wonderful gift

_____

Name_____

- A main verb tells what the subject is or does.

    He *visited* the bay.

- A **helping verb** helps another verb show an action. *Have,* *has,* and *had* are helping verbs. They help to tell about things that have already happened.

    The class *has* visited the bay.
    They *had* learned about spartina.
    I *have* looked for it in the water.

Circle the correct form of the verb to complete each sentence.

1. Spartina (have, has) turned into a problem.

2. It (has, have) lived in Washington since the 1800s.

3. Now it (has, have) turned into a pest.

4. Our neighbor (have, had) found some near his house.

5. It (have, had) destroyed his other plants.

6. It (has, have) forced native plants out of the area.

7. Sea creatures (has, have) moved out of there.

8. The mud flats (have, has) disappeared.

9. People (had, has) traveled with spartina from the East.

10. They (has, had) hoped it would be useful in the West.

11. People (have, has) tried many ways to control spartina.

12. We (had, has) to watch out for any signs of this plant.

13. I (have, has) to do more research on it.

14. Our neighbor (have, has) looked into some options.

15. Now we (has, have) found some useful information.

© Macmillan/McGraw-Hill

At Home: Have your child and a family member write present-tense sentences. Then have them trade sentences and rewrite them in the past tense using helping verbs.

- Verb forms of *be* are *is, are, am, was, were,* and *will.* They are also **helping verbs**.
- *Is, are,* and *am* help to tell about what is happening now.
   I *am* reading about plant life.
   Jeff *is* reading about plant life.
   We *are* reading about plant life.
- *Was* and *were* help to tell about what was happening in the past.
   I *was* learning about sea creatures last week.
   We *were* learning about sea creatures last week.
- *Will* helps to tell about something that will happen.
   We *will* visit the bay tomorrow.

Write a helping verb to finish each sentence.

1. Last week we _____ learning about spartina.

2. I _____ listening to Mr. Perkins.

3. Our teacher _____ talking about the problems in the bay.

4. Kim and I _____ doing a project about native bay life.

5. I _____ looking for good photos to use.

6. My classmates _____ finding lots of interesting information.

7. Joann and Ira _____ trying to find a way to use it all.

8. Kim _____ bringing her camera to the bay tomorrow.

9. Our friend _____ going to take her own pictures.

10. I _____ looking forward to revisiting the bay.

11. Tomorrow we _____ look for more spartina.

12. My classmate and I _____ walk in muddy water again.

 At Home: Have your child write three sentences about a park or other natural place he or she has visited. Ask your child to use helping verbs.

Name_____

> • Use quotation marks at the beginning and end of a person's exact words.

Write each line of dialogue correctly. Use the correct form of the irregular verb.

1. Has you heard about Washington's spartina problem? asked Kevin.

_____

_____

2. "I has read about it, but I hadn't actually seen any," said Mom.

_____

_____

3. My class have just learned about it said Kevin.

_____

_____

4. It have damaged many native plants said Mom.

_____

_____

5. We taked a trip to the bay to see the wildlife there said Kevin.

_____

_____

At Home: Have your child and a family member talk and write down each other's words using correct quotation marks and commas.

Washington Weed Whackers
Book 2/Unit 4

Name_____

> - **Helping verbs** help other verbs show an action.
> - Forms of *have—have, has,* and *had—*are used with verbs ending in *-ed*.
> - Forms of *be—is, are, was,* and *were—*are used with verbs ending in *-ing*.
> - *Will* helps to tell what will happen in the future.

Proofread the passage. Circle any incorrect helping verbs.

We has gotten on the buses very early at 7:00 a.m. We slept on the way to Padilla Bay. We finally arrived at 9:00 a.m.

"I has never been so tired! yawned Steph.

"Wake up! said Tory. I is planning to take a class picture."

"She have taken pictures at every class trip sighed Steph.

"Hurry up!" said Ms. Harper. We has a lot of activities planned for today.

Writing Activity

Rewrite the passage. Write the helping verbs correctly. Add commas and quotation marks where necessary.

_____

_____

_____

_____

_____

_____

_____

 At Home: Have your child and a family member take turns reading the above dialogue aloud, using the child's corrected version.

© Macmillan/McGraw-Hill

Name_____

Write the helping verb in each sentence.

1. Native plants have disappeared from the bay. _____

2. Spartina has destroyed them. _____

3. The plants were growing too large. _____

4. They have crowded out the other plants. _____

5. We will try to solve the problem. _____

6. We will start tomorrow. _____

7. We were looking for spartina. _____

8. I think we have found some. _____

Choose a helping verb from the box to complete each sentence. Some words may be used more than once.

am	is	are	was	were

9. Yesterday John and I _____ talking about the environment.

10. You _____ telling everyone about spartina.

11. Nick _____ going to the bay with me.

12. My friends _____ going to find spartina plants themselves.

13. I _____ bringing my video camera.

14. The students _____ looking everywhere.

15. I _____ focusing the lens on some plants.

- **Helping verbs** help other verbs show an action.
- Forms of *have—have, has,* and *had—*are used with verbs ending in *-ed*.
- Forms of *be—am, is, are, was,* and *were—*are used with verbs ending in *-ing*.

Mechanics

- Use quotation marks at the beginning and end of a person's exact words.
- Use a comma at the beginning or end of a person's exact words in a quotation.

Rewrite each sentence. Use the correct helping verb and the correct form of the action verb in the parentheses. Use quotation marks and commas correctly.

1. I be (tell) people about spartina said Caitlin.

_____

2. Allison and Jackson be (read) a book.

_____

3. Trina said I have (walk) all the way home.

_____

4. We be (talk) to a reporter, said Jane and Rob.

_____

5. They have (play) basketball in the gym.

_____

6. Mark and Jesse said Our class have (learn) about verbs.

_____

© Macmillan/McGraw-Hill

Name _____

> • Remember that an **irregular verb** has a special meaning to show the past tense.

Rewrite these sentences in the past tense.

1. We go to the zoo often during the summer.

_____

2. We see a special bird exhibit.

_____

3. The colorful birds sing loudly.

_____

4. They eat worms and seeds.

_____

5. I do visit the zoo often.

_____

Finish each sentence with the correct past-tense form of the verb.

6. We _____ to the zoo one morning.　　come　came

7. We _____ the polar bears being fed.　　see　saw

8. The zoo attendants _____ many　　say　said
animals live there.

9. She carefully _____ the food to　　give　gave
the bears.

10. The bears _____ with their big paws.　　eat　ate

At Home: Have your child choose three of the past-tense
verbs on this page. Ask him or her to write a short paragraph
using these words.

© Macmillan/McGraw-Hill

Name_____

- An **irregular verb** has a special spelling to show the past tense.
- Some **irregular verbs** have a special spelling when used with the helping verb *have*.

PRESENT	PAST	PAST
I do	I did	I have done
you see	you saw	you have seen
she comes	she came	she has come
we go	we went	we have gone
they bring	they brought	they have brought
I run	I ran	I have run
he gives	he gave	he has given
we sing	we sang	we have sung
they begin	they began	they have begun
I eat	I ate	I have eaten
it grows	it grew	it has grown

Write the correct past-tense form of the verb to finish the sentence.

1. come   People _____ to the zoo.

2. see   They _____ all the different animals.

3. sing   The birds had _____ for them a thousand times.

4. go   They _____ without thinking about the zoo's problems.

5. grow   They _____ bigger and bigger each year.

6. bring   She has _____ the zoo's problems to people's attention.

7. run   The newspaper _____ her letter.

8. give   Angel _____ a dollar to help the zoo.

9. do   Other people have _____ the same thing.

10. begin   Now the zoo has _____ to fix its problems.

 At Home: Have your child write three sentences about a visit to the zoo. Tell him or her to use the past-tense forms of three verbs from this page.

Name_____

- A present-tense verb tells what happens now.
- A past-tense verb tells about an action that already happened.
- A verb in the future tense tells about an action that is going to happen. To write about the future, use the special verb *will*.
- An irregular verb has a special spelling to show the past tense.
- Some irregular verbs have a special spelling when used with the helping verb *have*.

Rewrite the sentences using the correct form of the verb in parentheses.

1. I have (go) to the zoo twice before.

_____

2. My little brother Jeff (come) to the zoo with us.

_____

3. He (run) as fast as he could to see the chimpanzees.

_____

4. I have never (see) him look so surprised.

_____

5. Jeff (sing) a song back to the chimps.

_____

6. The zoo workers had (give) the chimps bananas.

_____

7. The chimps have (eat) bananas before.

_____

8. I have never (see) Jeff laugh so hard!

_____

© Macmillan/McGraw-Hill

At Home: Have your child create sentences that use irregular verbs from this page in the past, present, and future forms.

- An irregular verb has a special spelling to show the past tense.
- Some irregular verbs have a special spelling when used with the helping verb *have*.

Proofread the paragraphs. Circle any incorrect irregular verbs.

In class, we read about Angel Arellano. She seen that the Chaffee Zoo was having money problems. She worried about the animals at the zoo. She wrote a letter to her local newspaper. It bringed attention to the zoo. Angel have a suggestion. She has gave a dollar to the zoo. She hoped everyone else would give a dollar, too. People begun to donate money. It helped the zoo survive.

We wondered what we could change. If we all given a dollar, who could we help?

Writing Activity

Rewrite the paragraphs. Write the irregular verbs correctly. Make sure other verbs are also written in the correct tense.

_____

_____

_____

_____

_____

_____

_____

_____

 At Home: Have your child write five sentences containing irregular verbs.

Choose the verb form that goes with *have* or *had*. Mark your answer.

1. We have _____ on trips to the zoo.
   a. gone   b. go   c. went

2. I had _____ something special there this time.
   a. done   b. do   c. did

3. The zoo keepers had _____ us a tour of the zoo.
   a. give   b. given   c. gave

4. My friends and I have _____ how the zoo workers keep the zoo running.
   a. see   b. seen   c. saw

5. They had _____ to the end of the tour and thanked the zoo keepers.
   a. comes   b. came   c. come

Choose the correct past-tense form.

6. Yesterday we _____ to the zoo to see the new panda bears.
   a. go   b. gone   c. went

7. The bears _____ to the zoo from China.
   a. come   b. came   c. comes

8. The people there _____ the bears as a gift to our zoo.
   a. give   b. given   c. gave

9. I _____ the bears in their new zoo habitat.
   a. see   b. seen   c. saw

10. They _____ bamboo shoots and stared at us.
    a. ate   b. eat   c. eaten

11. We were pleased that we _____ to the zoo.
    a. come   b. came   c. comes

12. Other plants and trees _____ in the habitat.
    a. grows   b. grew   c. grown

Name_____

- An **irregular verb** has a special spelling to show the past tense.
- Some **irregular verbs** have a special spelling when used with the helping verb *have*.

Look at the picture and read the paragraph. Look for mistakes with past-tense verbs. Rewrite the paragraph on the lines below.

Our zoo have a special event last week. It stayed open late one night. We had never see the zoo in the dark. My family gone that night. We bring our friends Jake and Shana, too. The elephants and giraffes was still awake.

_____

_____

_____

_____

_____

_____

_____

Name_____

- A **contraction** is a shortened form of two words.
- An **apostrophe** (') shows where one or more letters have been left out. In most contractions with *not*, the apostrophe takes the place of *o*.

is not	isn't	have not	haven't
are not	aren't	had not	hadn't
was not	wasn't	do not	don't
were not	weren't	does not	doesn't
has not	hasn't	did not	didn't

- *Can't* and *won't* are different. The apostrophe in *can't* takes the place of two letters: *n* and *o*. In *won't*, three letters disappear and the *o* changes position

cannot	can't
will not	won't

Circle the contraction in each sentence. Write the words that form the contraction.

1. I don't have my own room yet. _____

2. We didn't have time to finish it. _____

3. I can't get any peace and quiet! _____

4. I won't complain. _____

5. We haven't much left to do. _____

6. Dad just hasn't had time to finish my room. _____

7. We weren't expecting a difficult task! _____

8. I hadn't known much about a building before now. _____

9. We aren't going to quit. _____

10. It doesn't take long if we work together. _____

© Macmillan/McGraw-Hill

At Home: Ask your child and a family member to take turns writing sentences with the contractions on this page.

Name_____

- A **contraction** is a shortened form of two words
- An **apostrophe** (') shows where one or more letters have been left out. In most contractions with *not*, the apostrophe takes the place of *o*.

Rewrite each sentence using a contraction in place of the underlined verb and *not*.

1. I <u>did</u> <u>not</u> want to share a room with my brothers.

_____

2. There <u>was</u> <u>not</u> enough space for all of us.

_____

3. There <u>is</u> <u>not</u> a place in the house for me to call my own.

_____

4. At first, we <u>were</u> <u>not</u> sure what to do.

_____

5. "I <u>do</u> <u>not</u> mind using the storage room," I told Mom.

_____

6. "I <u>will</u> <u>not</u> mind," said Mom.

_____

7. I <u>have</u> <u>not</u> had a room of my own yet.

_____

8. I <u>was</u> <u>not</u> sure how to fix it up.

_____

9. I <u>will</u> <u>not</u> have a bed until tomorrow.

_____

 At Home: Have your child look in books or magazines for contractions. Have your child write down the contractions he or she finds and the words that form those contractions.

Name _____

> • An **apostrophe** takes the place of letters left out of a contraction.

Rewrite these sentences. Add apostrophes to the contractions.

1. My part of the room isnt like my sisters' part.

_____

2. You cant find any empty space on her walls.

_____

3. There isnt room for another poster or photograph.

_____

4. There arent any posters or pictures on my wall.

_____

5. I dont need anything but paint and a brush.

_____

6. I didnt paint pictures.

_____

7. I havent painted anything but colorful shapes.

_____

8. Eileen and Leah say it doesnt make sense.

_____

9. I hadnt meant for my wall to look perfect.

_____

10. I wont mind as long as its my very own space.

_____

At Home: Have your child write five sentences with contractions.

- A **contraction** is a shortened form of two words.
- An **apostrophe** (') shows where one or more letters have been left out.

Proofread these paragraphs. Circle any contractions that are not correctly written. Add the apostrophes where they belong.

Its very difficult to share a room. You dont have any space of your own. You cant ever have the whole place to yourself. I had this problem. I shared my room with my brothers. They came in and played when I tried to do homework. We fought all the time. I didnt have a way to get away from everyone!

Then I had an idea. Our attic hadnt been used much. Mom and Dad said that they werent planning to use all the space. I cleared out an area in the attic. I put up curtains to make it private. I found old furniture that wasnt being used. Suddenly I had an office. Its my own special place. Best of all, my brothers and I arent fighting anymore! So if you havent got a place of your own, look around. There might be a special place just waiting for you to find it!

Writing Activity

Write a short poem that describes a space of your own. Use at least two contractions.

_____

_____

_____

_____

_____

© Macmillan/McGraw-Hill

At Home: Have your child write six lines of dialogue that use contractions.

Name_____

Write the contraction for each pair of words.

1. does not _____

2. will not _____

3. cannot _____

4. have not _____

5. are not _____

6. did not _____

7. is not _____

8. do not _____

9. were not _____

10. has not _____

11. had not _____

12. was not _____

Write the words that form the contraction in each sentence.

13. I hadn't ever lived alone. _____

14. I don't remember ever being alone. _____

15. I wasn't sure what a room of my own would be like. _____

16. Now I can't imagine going back to sharing! _____

17. How come you haven't had that problem? _____

18. I didn't get much furniture. _____

19. My room doesn't have any pictures on the walls. _____

20. My sisters aren't allowed to barge into my room _____

Name_____

- A **contraction** is a shortened form of two words.
- An **apostrophe** (') shows where one or more letters have been left out.

Mechanics

- Add an apostrophe to take the place of the letters left out of a contraction.
- Add an apostrophe to take the place of the letter *o* in words with *not* to form a contraction.
- Remember that sometimes an apostrophe takes the place of more than one letter in words with *not*.

Write the correct contraction on the line.

1. I havent lived in my new room long. _____

2. We did not finish writing the poem. _____

3. I have a lamp but dont have a table for it. _____

4. Jill has not given in her homework _____

5. My chair is nice, but it does not have any pillows. _____

6. The sun isnt that hot today. _____

7. She will not go to the doctor today. _____

8. After eating we were not able to swim. _____

Name _____

Read the passage and look at the underlined parts. Is there a mistake? If so, how do you correct it? Mark your answer.

It was a hot July afternoon. <u>We was trying to make strawberry shortcake.</u>
                                    (1)

We had never made one before. The kitchen was very warm, though. Steve said the butter was melting. Beth said that *she* was melting! The oven was making the room even hotter. <u>We were eating the cake in front of a fan.</u> Next
                                    (2)

time, we will wait for a cool day!

1. **A.** Change *was* to *is*.
   B. Change *was* to *am*.
   C. Change *was* to *were*.
   D. No mistake.

2. **E.** Change *was* to *is*.
   F. Change *was* to *am*.
   G. Change *was* to *were*.
   H. No mistake.

<u>The annual block party were on July 4 this year.</u> There were more people
                        (3)

there than ever before. <u>Our family were in charge of games and contests.</u>
                                    (4)

We had a lot of great ideas. My favorites were the relay race and the pet beauty contest. They were fun!

3. **A.** Change *were* to *is*.
   B. Change *were* to *was*.
   C. Change *were* to *are*.
   D. No mistake.

4. **E.** Change *were* to *was*.
   F. Change *were* to *am*.
   G. Change *were* to *be*.
   H. No mistake.

Name _____

Our zoo had a big party. It was a way to raise money to improve the zoo. I went with my family. <u>Our next door neighbors comed with us.</u>
(5)

<u>We were gave a special tour of the zoo.</u> We saw how they take care of the
(6)
animals every day. We plan to go back again soon!

5. A. Change *come* to *comes*.
   B. Change *come* to *camed*.
   C. Change *comed* to *came*.
   D. No mistake

6. E. Change *gave* to *given*.
   F. Change *gave* to *gaved*.
   G. Change *gave* to *gives*.
   H. No mistake

My family had just moved into our new house. We hadn't unpacked much yet. The rooms didn't have any furniture. <u>There isn't any pictures on the walls.</u>
(7)

The windows didn't have any curtains or blinds. Mom said it would take a lot of work to put it all together. <u>I weren't complaining, though.</u> For the first
(8)
time, I was going to have my own room!

7. A. Change *isn't* to *wasn't*.
   B. Change *isn't* to *hasn't*.
   C. Change *isn't* to *weren't*.
   D. No mistake.

8. E. Change *weren't* to *aren't*.
   F. Change *weren't* to *isn't*.
   G. Change *weren't* to *wasn't*.
   H. No mistake.

© Macmillan/McGraw-Hill

Name_____

> - A **pronoun** is a word that takes the place of one or more nouns.
> - A **singular pronoun** replaces a singular noun.
> - First person singular pronouns are *I* and *me;* the second person singular pronoun is *you;* the third person singular pronouns are *he, she, it, him,* and *her.*
>   Example: *Boom Town* takes place in the 1800s. It takes place in the 1800s.

Read the sentences. Write the singular pronoun or pronouns you find in each sentence.

1. James gave me the book *Boom Town*. _____

2. He says it makes him want to live back in the Old West.

   _____

3. I read it from cover to cover in one afternoon. _____

4. I will tell you that it is about a girl named Amanda. _____

5. She starts a pie-selling business. _____

6. Many people buy pies from her. _____

7. I read how she gets other people to start businesses and help the town.

   _____

8. It makes me want to start a business, too! _____

9. Maybe I could open a bakery. _____

10. I could open it with my mom. _____

© Macmillan/McGraw-Hill

 At Home: Have your child write four sentences with singular pronouns.

Name_____

• Plural pronouns are *we, you, they, us,* and *them*.

Read each pair of sentences. Replace the underlined word or words with a plural pronoun. Use clues in the sentences to help you decide.

1. <u>James, Sarah, and I</u> decided to start a cookie business.

_____

2. Have <u>you and your friends</u> ever tried to start a business?

_____

3. <u>James and Sarah</u> made the cookies. _____

4. I painted signs while I waited for <u>James and Sarah</u>. _____

5. Then there was a phone call for <u>James, Sarah, and me</u>.

_____

6. <u>James, Sarah, and I</u> had our first customers! _____

7. <u>The cookies</u> were still warm from the oven. _____

8. Sarah carefully wrapped <u>the cookies</u>. _____

9. <u>James, Sarah, and I</u> delivered the cookies to our customers.

_____

10. <u>The people</u> were delighted and promised to order more.

_____

 At Home: Tell your child a story about what you did yesterday. Have your child write down any plural pronouns that are used.

Name_____

> • A **proper noun** names a special person, place, or thing.
> • A proper noun begins with a capital letter.
> • The pronoun *I* is always capitalized.

**Rewrite each sentence correctly. Write each proper noun and /
with a capital letter.**

1. In the book *Boom Town*, amanda starts a pie-selling business.

_____

_____

2. Like amanda, i live in california.

_____

3. My family has a bakery in the town of marlton.

_____

4. It is called the little red bakery.

_____

5. It is in a red building on maple street.

_____

6. My brother chris works there with mom and dad.

_____

7. Our biggest seller is a pie called the incredible peach experience.

_____

_____

8. I like to bring my friends steve and rebecca to the bakery.

_____

_____

© Macmillan/McGraw-Hill

At Home: Have your child look around the kitchen. Ask your
child to make a list of the things he or she can name with
proper nouns.

Name_____

> - A **pronoun** is a word that takes the place of one or more nouns.
> - A **singular pronoun** replaces a singular noun. A **plural pronoun** replaces a plural noun or more than one noun.
> - Singular pronouns are *I, you, he, she, it, me, him,* and *her*.
> - Plural pronouns are *we, you, they, us,* and *them*.

Proofread the paragraph. Circle any incorrect pronouns.

We recently read *Boom Town*. They is the story of a girl named amanda. Her helped her town grow by starting a pie business. Us decided to try the gooseberry pie recipe in the book. Mom suggested using blueberries instead. Then Mom thought there wasn't enough sugar. Him kept adding more. I thought there weren't enough berries. You piled them so high that there wasn't enough dough to cover them. Then me forgot to turn on the oven. No wonder the pie took so long to bake!

Rewrite the paragraph with the correct pronouns. Make sure all proper nouns and *I* are capitalized.

_____

_____

_____

_____

_____

_____

_____

© Macmillan/McGraw-Hill

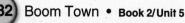

At Home: Have your child find a paragraph in a magazine. Ask him or her to rewrite it using pronouns where there are proper nouns.

Name _____

**A. Write *yes* if the underlined word is a pronoun.
Write *no* if the underlined word is not a pronoun.**

1. Have <u>you</u> read about Amanda and her pie business? _____

2. <u>She</u> started making gooseberry pies for the settlers in California.

 _____

3. They <u>bought</u> many pies from Amanda. _____

4. The settlers in her town realized <u>there</u> was a need for other businesses.

 _____

5. Amanda helped <u>them</u> think of ideas. _____

6. <u>Soon</u> they had built a busy town. _____

B. Underline the pronoun in each sentence. Then write *S* if it is singular or *P* if it is plural.

7. We visited a museum over the weekend. _____

8. The guide showed us how people lived during the California Gold Rush.

 _____

9. She said that towns sprang up where people searched for gold.

 _____

10. I had read about the Gold Rush in the book *Boom Town*.

 _____

11. It has become one of my favorite books. _____

12. We read it during class _____

Name_____

> • A **pronoun** is a word that takes the place of one or more nouns.
> • A pronoun must match the noun that it replaces.
> • Singular pronouns are *I, you, he, she, it, me, him,* and *her*.
> • Plural pronouns are *we, you, they, us,* and *them*.

Look at the pictures. Read the sentences. Replace the underlined word with the correct pronoun.

1. Her moved to California. _____

2. Amanda baked pies for they. _____

3. Them bought Amanda's pies. _____

4. Amanda's brothers helped she. _____

5. The pie business kept she busy. _____

6. Amanda gave he an idea. _____

7. Him opened a trading post. _____

8. People said, "Look how Amanda's pies have helped we!"

_____

Name_____

> • Use a **subject pronoun** as the subject of a sentence.
> • *I, you, he she, it, we,* and *they* are subject pronouns.

Read the sentences. Choose the correct pronoun in parentheses to complete each sentence. Write the pronoun.

1. My brother, sister, and _____ visited our aunt's farm this summer. (me, I)

2. _____ was very different from where we live. (It, Them)

3. _____ each had our favorite animals. (Us, We)

4. _____ liked the roosters in the yard. (He, Him)

5. _____ preferred the little goats. (Her, She)

6. Have _____ ever seen a baby goat? (you, your)

7. _____ followed us around like puppies. (They, Them)

8. Could _____ have one as a pet? (we, us)

9. My aunt says _____ eat a lot. (they, them)

10. _____ feeds them three times a day. (Her, She)

11. "Why don't _____ ask Uncle Ben for help?" I asked. (your, you)

12. "_____ is busy feeding the cows," she said. (He, Him)

At Home: Have your child write sentences about farm animals. Have him or her write each sentence with a subject pronoun.

Name_____

> • Use an **object pronoun** after an action verb or after a word such as *for, at, of, with,* or *to.*
> • *Me, you, him, her, it, us,* and *them* are object pronouns.

Read the sentences. Choose the correct pronoun in parentheses to complete each sentence. Write the pronoun.

1. Ms. Robinson read _____ Beatrice's Goat. (us, we)

2. It is about a girl named Beatrice and the goat given (her, she)

   to _____.

3. The story showed how Beatrice's family took the (it, its)

   goat's milk and sold _____ to raise money.

4. Beatrice's family used the money to send (her, she)

   _____ to school.

5. Josh listened to the story with _____. (I, me)

6. I told _____ I had met some goats last (he, him)
   summer at a farm.

7. We played with _____ a lot while we (they, them)
   were there.

8. "I will show _____ a picture of a baby (you, your)
   goat," I said.

At Home: Have your child look in the pages of a book or magazine. Ask him or her to write down all the object pronouns he or she finds.

© Macmillan/McGraw-Hill

Name_____

> • Use a **subject pronoun** as the subject of a sentence.
> • *I, you, he, she, it, we,* and *they* are subject pronouns.
> • Use an **object pronoun** after an action verb or after a word such as *for, at, of, with,* or *to.*
> • *Me, you, him, her, it, us,* and *them* are object pronouns.

Replace each underlined word or group of words in each sentence with the correct subject or object pronoun. Write the new sentences.

1. <u>Mom and Dad</u> took <u>Tim and me</u> to a petting zoo.

_____

2. <u>A sign</u> explained how to behave with <u>the animals</u>.

_____

3. <u>Tim</u> petted <u>a baby goat</u>.

_____

4. <u>Two other goats</u> came along and poked at <u>Tim and me</u>.

_____

5. <u>Mom</u> told <u>Tim</u> that they were looking for food.

_____

6. <u>Tim</u> said to <u>Mom and me</u>, "I hope they don't think I'm lunch!"

_____

7. <u>Dad</u> took a picture of <u>Tim and the goats</u>.

_____

8. Should I send <u>you and Grandma</u> a picture of the goats?

_____

At Home: Have your child write a paragraph about meeting an animal. Have him or her circle all the subject pronouns and underline all the object pronouns.

© Macmillan/McGraw-Hill

Name_____

- Use a **subject pronoun** as the subject of a sentence.
- *I, you, he, she, it, we,* and *they* are subject pronouns.
- Use an **object pronoun** after an action verb or after a word such as *for, at, of, with,* or *to.*
- *Me, you, him, her, it, us,* and *them* are object pronouns.

Proofread the paragraphs below. Circle any pronouns that are used incorrectly.

    My class read a book called *Beatrice's Goat.* Us learned how the gift of a goat from Heifer International helped Beatrice go to school. The book had an influence on we all. Everyone wanted to do something to help others.

    We decided to make and sell farm animal pins. Everyone in town loved they. Them helped the class raise a lot of money. We were glad to give the money to Heifer International. We felt good—we were helping they. Maybe yous can help someone, too!

Rewrite the paragraph. Write the pronouns correctly.

_____

_____

_____

_____

_____

_____

_____

At Home: Have a family member proofread your child's rewritten paragraphs.

Name_____

Read the first sentence in each set. One of the four sentences that follow it correctly replaces the underlined words. Circle the correct sentence.

1. <u>Our goat Annie</u> lives in the small barn behind our house.

   A. They lives in the small barn behind our house.

   B. You lives in the small barn behind our house.

   C. Them lives in the small barn behind our house.

   D. It lives in the small barn behind our house.

2. Annie eats breakfast with <u>my family</u> every morning.

   A. She eats breakfast with us every morning.

   B. Her eats breakfast with us every morning.

   C. We eats breakfast with her every morning.

   D. They eats breakfast with us every morning.

3. <u>Dad</u> listens for <u>Annie's hooves</u> tapping on the porch.

   A. We listens for it tapping on the porch.

   B. He listens for them tapping on the porch.

   C. He listens for they tapping on the porch.

   D. I listens for her tapping on the porch.

4. <u>My parents</u> feed <u>Annie</u> a mix of different foods.

   A. Us feed them a mix of different foods.

   B. They feed him a mix of different foods.

   C. You feed us a mix of different foods.

   D. They feed her a mix of different foods.

5. <u>Goats</u> will eat anything <u>yous</u> give them!

   A. We will eat anything you give them!

   B. She will eat anything you give them!

   C. It will eat anything we give them!

   D. They will eat anything you give them!

- Use a **subject pronoun** as the subject of a sentence.
- *I, you, he, she, it, we,* and *they* are subject pronouns.
- Use an **object pronoun** after an action verb or after a word such as for, at, of, with, or to.
- *Me, you, him, her, it, us,* and *them* are object pronouns.

Look at the pictures. Proofread and rewrite the sentences correctly.

1. What do yous know about goats?
Them have lived with we for a long
time. People herded it as far back
as 12,000 years ago.

_____

_____

_____

2. Explorers took goats on long ocean trips.
Them kept they for fresh milk. Them
found it was easy to take care of it.

_____

_____

_____

3. A goat will not really eat a tin can.
This goat is just testing its. Them
are curious about they.

_____

_____

_____

Name_____

> • A **possessive pronoun** takes the place of a possessive noun. It shows who or what owns something.
> • Some possessive pronouns are used before nouns. These include *my, your, his, her, its, our,* and *their*.

Write the possessive pronoun on the line.

1. Riverbank State Park in New York City is famous for its carousel.

   _____

2. Milo Mottola told people about his idea for the carousel.

   _____

3. He asked his art students to draw animals for the carousel.

   _____

4. Their designs were used to make the carousel. _____

5. Our class plans to take a trip to the park. _____

6. Lily wants to see the animal designed by her cousin. _____

7. My mother told me to take a picture of the carousel. _____

8. Will your class go on any trips this year? _____

9. This is the first trip for our class this year. _____

10. My father is going on the trip with us. _____

At Home: Ask your child to use possessive pronouns to write descriptions of his or her favorite animals.

Name_____

- Some possessive pronouns can stand alone. These include *mine, yours, his, hers, its, ours, yours,* and *theirs*.

Read the sentences and the possessive pronouns in parentheses. Write the correct possessive pronoun.

1. The students in _____ class are designing carousels. (our, ours)

2. I am almost finished with _____. (my, mine)

3. Did you finish _____? (your, yours)

4. Nina and Nick showed me _____ designs. (their, theirs)

5. Nina used dinosaurs in _____. (her, hers)

6. Nick put only birds in _____ carousel. (his, their)

7. I liked both of _____. (their, theirs)

8. Each carousel had _____ own style. (its, their)

9. _____ carousel would be different from anyone else's design. (Your, Yours)

10. All of _____ are different. (our, ours)

11. I hope the teacher likes _____! (my, mine)

12. _____ class has worked really hard. (Our, Ours)

 At Home: Have your child write four sentences that each use a possessive pronoun before a noun.

© Macmillan/McGraw-Hill

Name_____

> • A possessive pronoun can replace a possessive noun.
> • Use these possessive pronouns before nouns: *my, your, his, her, its, our, their.*
> • Use these possessive pronouns alone: *mine, yours, his, hers, its, ours, theirs.*

Circle the correct possessive pronoun in the parentheses.

1. Mrs. Parker asked (her, hers) students to design a carousel.

2. The students are all drawing (their, theirs) favorite animals.

3. Mario said (his, his's) is the elephant.

4. Tomas and Kwan said (their, theirs) is the crocodile.

5. Some of us are using (our, ours) imaginations to create interesting animals.

6. (My, Mine) animal is a green tiger with wings.

7. I colored (its, it's) wings purple.

8. David says (your, yours) drawing is the best.

9. We like (your, yours) a lot, too.

10. I told Sola (her, hers) is very colorful.

© Macmillan/McGraw-Hill

At Home: Have your child write sentences with possessive nouns. Have him or her rewrite the sentences using possessive pronouns.

- A **possessive pronoun** takes the place of a possessive noun. It shows who or what owns something.
- Some possessive pronouns are used before nouns. These include *my, your, his, her, its, our, your,* and *their*.
- Some possessive pronouns can stand alone. These include *mine, yours, his, hers, its, ours,* and *theirs*.

Rewrite this journal entry. Be sure to correct the pronouns and nouns.

We visited ours relatives in New York City this summer. Mine cousin Tracy took we to Riverbank State Park, along the Hudson River. Her showed us an unusual carousel in the park. The octopus had two heads. The zebra was plaid. The lion was green. She explained that the carousels animals were all designed by local kids. Tracy pointed out how the artists signature is engraved beneath each animal.

_____

_____

_____

_____

_____

_____

_____

_____

© Macmillan/McGraw-Hill

 At Home: Have your child write a personal narrative about a trip to a park or playground. Check your child's work.

Name_____

A. Write *yes* if the underlined word is a possessive pronoun.
Write *no* if the underlined word is not a possessive pronoun.

1. Milo Mottola asked kids in his neighborhood to design the carousel.

_____

2. The kids became Mottola's art students. _____

3. He chose 32 of their drawings for the actual carousel.

_____

4. All the students hoped that one of theirs would be chosen.

_____

5. The artist's signature was engraved beneath each of the animals.

_____

B. Write *yes* if the underlined word is the correct possessive
pronoun. Write *no* if the underlined word is not the correct
possessive pronoun.

6. Our class took a trip to an amusement park. _____

7. Mine favorite ride is the roller coaster. _____

8. Cara said that hers is the waterslide. _____

9. George said his's is the carousel. _____

10. I said I would try their favorites if they would try mine.

_____

- A **possessive pronoun** takes the place of a possessive noun. It shows who or what owns something.
- Some possessive pronouns are used before nouns. These include *my, your, his, her, its, our, your,* and *their*.
- Some possessive pronouns can stand alone. These include *mine, yours, his, hers, its, ours,* and *theirs*.

Read each sentence. Then write each one with the correct possessive pronoun.

1. What is yours favorite thing to do on a vacation?

_____

2. Mine family visits a different theme park every summer.

_____

3. Sam has his' own idea of the perfect theme park.

_____

4. There would be only roller coasters in his's.

_____

5. Sandra said that her would have water rides and a zoo.

_____

6. I would have a mix of everything in mine's.

_____

7. That ride is fun because of it's fast speed.

_____

8. Next vacation my sister and I will visit ours favorite theme park.

_____

9. What will you do on your?

_____

10. The Johnsons go to the beach on theirs vacation.

_____

Name_____

> • A **present-tense** verb must agree with its **subject pronoun**.
> • Add -s or -es to most action verbs when you use the pronouns *he, she,* and *it.*
> • Do not add -s or -es to an action verb in the present tense when you use the pronouns *I, we, you,* and *they.*

Choose the correct verb to complete each sentence. Write the verb.

1. I (deliver, delivers) newspapers every day with my brother.

_____

2. Some days it (rain, rains). _____

3. Then we (get, gets) a ride from Mom. _____

4. She (drive, drives) from house to house. _____

5. I (open, opens) the window of the car. _____

6. He (throw, throws) the newspapers onto the driveways.

_____

7. It (take, takes) less time on sunny days. _____

8. Then we (walk, walks) down the streets and see our customers.

_____

9. They (wave, waves) to us. _____

10. Do you (read, reads) a newspaper every day? _____

At Home: Ask your child to write three sentences using present-tense verbs.

Name_____

- A present-tense verb must agree with its subject pronoun.
- Add -s or -es to most present-tense action verbs when using the pronouns *he, she,* and *it.*
- Do not add -s or -es to most present-tense action verbs when using the pronouns *I, we, you,* and *they.*

Circle the correct present-tense verb to complete each sentence.

1. I (work, works) on our school newspaper.

2. It (discuss, discusses) important issues in our community.

3. We (write, writes) many stories for our newspaper.

4. He (write, writes) the funniest stories each week.

5. You (learn, learns) many things when you work on a newspaper.

6. She (help, helps) us to improve our writing.

7. They (know, knows) people who work at real newspapers.

8. We (take, takes) photographs with a camera.

9. They (read, reads) newspapers every day.

10. You (like, likes) to read our interviews.

 At Home: Have your child and a family member each say
four sentences with a pronoun and its form of *have* or *be.*

Name _____

> - A present-tense verb must agree with its subject pronoun.
> - Add -s to most action verbs when you use the pronouns *he, she,* and *it*.
> - Do not add -s to an action verb in the present tense when you use the pronouns *I, we, you,* and *they*.

Write the correct present-tense verb to complete each sentence.

1. We _____ the newspaper at the store.　　(buy, buys)

2. I _____ at the sports section first.　　(look, looks)

3. She _____ the news section in the morning.　　(read, reads)

4. It _____ readers what is happening in the city.　　(tell, tells)

5. We _____ sections when we are done reading.　　(trade, trades)

6. They _____ hard at the newspaper.　　(work, works)

7. He _____ vocabulary words he does not know.　　(circle, circles)

8. You _____ information from newspapers and magazines.　　(get, gets)

9. They _____ to talk about the news stories.　　(like, likes)

10. She _____ a computer when she writes.　　(use, uses)

At Home: Have your child write a short newspaper article about an event at his or her school. Have your child draw a line connecting subject pronouns with their verbs.

Name_____

> • A **present-tense** verb must agree with its **subject pronoun**.
> • Add *-s* or *-es* to most action verbs when you use the pronouns *he, she,* and *it*.
> • Do not add *-s* or *-es* to an action verb in the present tense when you use the pronouns *I, we, you,* and *they*.

Proofread the paragraph. Circle any verbs that do not agree with their pronouns.

   This summer my's best friend and I are doing something new. We puts out our own newspaper every week. It be only four pages long, but it take a lot of time to do it well. I are in charge of the stories. Curt takes all the pictures. Each week, we has to find new stories for our paper. I talk to people in town. I looks for interesting things. He take his's camera everywhere. We has more pictures than pages!

Writing Activity

Rewrite the paragraph. Make sure the verbs agree with their pronouns. Fix any incorrect possessive pronouns.

_____

_____

_____

_____

_____

_____

_____

At Home: Have your child read an article in a newspaper. Ask him or her to point out examples of pronoun-verb agreement.

© Macmillan/McGraw-Hill

Name_____

A. Read each group of sentences. Circle the one with the subject pronoun that does not agree with the action verb.

1. **A.** We deliver the newspaper every day.

   B. He folds the newspapers.

   C. I toss the papers onto the porches.

   D. They brings them inside.

2. **A.** We read different sections of the newspaper.

   B. I likes the movie reviews.

   C. She enjoys the crossword puzzles.

   D. On Sunday it takes all morning to read the paper.

3. **A.** They read the newspaper.

   B. It gives me information.

   C. We learns about our community.

   D. You get more knowledge about events.

B. Read the sentences. Choose the correct verb form to complete each sentence. Write the correct verb on the line.

4. I _____ the editor of our school newspaper.

   A. know   **C.** visits

   B. likes   **D.** are

5. We _____ new stories every week.

   A. has   **C.** creates

   B. shows   **D.** write

6. They _____ news about our school.

   A. says   **C.** give

   B. is   **D.** presents

© Macmillan/McGraw-Hill

Name_____

- A **present-tense** verb must agree with its **subject pronoun**.
- Add -*s* or -*es* to most action verbs when you use the pronouns *he, she,* and *it.*
- Do not add -*s* or -*es* to an action verb in the present tense when you use the pronouns *I, we, you,* and *they.*

Read each sentence aloud. Change the underlined verbs to make them agree with the subject pronouns. Write the sentences.

1. It <u>take</u> many people to put out a daily newspaper.

_____

2. They <u>needs</u> to work quickly.

_____

3. The newspaper <u>seem</u> new every day.

_____

4. He <u>pick</u> stories for the front page.

_____

5. She <u>check</u> facts in the stories.

_____

6. I <u>has</u> an idea for a newspaper story.

_____

7. He <u>need</u> to <u>takes</u> pictures.

_____

8. We <u>works</u> hard to <u>meets</u> deadlines.

_____

Name_____

- A **contraction** is a shortened form of two words.
- An **apostrophe** ['] replaces letters that are left out.

I am = I'm	we are = we're	I have = I've
he is = he's	you are = you're	you have = you've
she is = she's	they are = they're	we have = we've
it is = it's		they have = they've

Rewrite each sentence and replace the underlined words with a contraction.

1. <u>We are</u> learning about animal homes.

_____

2. <u>They are</u> different for each kind of animal.

_____

3. <u>It is</u> important for animals to have the right place.

_____

4. <u>I am</u> fascinated by many of the animals' homes.

_____

5. My brother says that <u>we have</u> seen otters on the riverbank.

_____

_____

6. <u>He is</u> hoping to see the otters come out of their home.

_____

7. <u>We are</u> bringing a camera to the river.

_____

8. <u>You are</u> going to get copies of all the pictures!

_____

At Home: Have your child write a short description of his or her home. Ask your child to use contractions with pronouns.

Animal Homes • **Book 2/Unit 5** (153)

© Macmillan/McGraw-Hill

Name

- Remember, a **contraction** is a shortened form of two words.
- An **apostrophe** ['] replaces letters that are left out.
  Here are more contractions.

I have = I've	I will = I'll	we will = we'll
you have = you've	he will = he'll	you will = you'll
we have = we've	she will = she'll	they will = they'll
they have = they've	it will = it'll	

Underline the two words in each sentence that you can make into a contraction. Then write each sentence with the contraction.

1. We have seen two beavers building a home in our pond.

_____

2. It will be fun to watch them work.

_____

3. You will see them when you come over.

_____

4. I have read about beavers and their homes.

_____

5. She will find branches for their home.

_____

6. He will build with branches and mud.

_____

7. They will build an underwater door to their home.

_____

8. They have lots of building to do!

_____

 At Home: Have your child and a family member take turns asking each other questions with pronouns.

Name_____

> - A **contraction** is a shortened form of two words. An **apostrophe** replaces letters that are left out.
>   Examples: *I'm, he's, it's, we'll, they've*
> - A **possessive pronoun** takes the place of a possessive noun. It shows who or what owns something.
>   Examples: *my, his, its, our, their*

Circle the correct word to complete each sentence. Write C if the answer is a contraction and P if the answer is a possessive pronoun.

1. (Its, It's) possible that anmals live near your home. _____

2. (Your, You're) lucky if you find animals to watch. _____

3. (I've, Iv'e) spent a lot of time watching animals near my home. _____

4. We've seen birds build nests in the tree in (our, our's) yard. _____

5. My neighbor said he's seen rabbit holes near (he's, his) house. _____

6. Now (we're, were) watching a squirrel build a nest in a tree. _____

7. Mom said the squirrel wants to hide (it's, its) nuts in the nest. _____

8. (Well, We'll) make sure to tell you when the nest is finished. _____

9. (I'll, It'll) be fun to watch the squirrels work. _____

10. The animals look in the fields for (their, they're) food. _____

© Macmillan/McGraw-Hill

 At Home: Have your child write sentences that include both a contraction and a sound-alike possessive pronoun.

Name_____

> • A **contraction** is a shortened form of two words.
> • An **apostrophe** ['] replaces letters that are left out.

Proofread the paragraph. Circle any incorrectly written contractions.

    Im planning to become a zoologist someday. That's someone who studies animals. Until then I can learn a lot by watching and reading about animals. There are plenty of rabbits in our backyard. Theyve built their warren near our fence. Ive seen rabbits hop across the yard. Then suddenly theyre gone down the hole into the warren. I cant go down there, so I read about what its like inside.

Writing Activity

Rewrite the paragraph. Write each contraction with the apostrophe in the right place. Make sure possessive pronouns and contractions are used correctly.

_____

_____

_____

_____

_____

_____

_____

At Home: Have your child call out 9 contractions he or she knows and write them on a piece of paper.

Name_____

A. Is the underlined contraction correctly written? Write *yes* if it is. Write *no* if it is not and then write the word correctly.

1. <u>Were</u> buying a new cage for our hamster. _____

2. <u>Its</u> going to have tunnels for him to crawl through. _____

3. <u>He's</u> going to have a lot of fun playing in the tunnels. _____

4. <u>It'll</u> be like the tunnels he would dig in the desert. _____

5. <u>I'm</u> looking forward to seeing him play. _____

B. Write the contraction for the underlined words.

6. <u>You are</u> not going to believe this. _____

7. <u>We have</u> got an owl living in a tree in our yard. _____

8. <u>It is</u> the biggest bird I have ever seen. _____

9. <u>You will</u> have to come over and see it sometime. _____

10. My sister says <u>she is</u> going to videotape it flying. _____

11. I hope <u>it will</u> stay all summer. _____

12. <u>It is</u> very fun to watch it fly. _____

Name_____

> • A contraction is a shortened form of two words.

Mechanics

> • An apostrophe takes the place of letters.
> • Possessive pronouns do not have apostrophes.
> • Do not confuse possessive pronouns with contractions.

Look at the picture. Read the sentences. Write the sentences correctly.

1. Its a picture of those two beaver's dam.

_____

2. Theyve built it in the middle of the stream.

_____

3. Itll block the flow of water.

_____

4. Theyre able to enter it from underwater.

_____

5. Theyll keep adding more branches and stones.

_____

Name_____

Read each passage. Choose a word or group of words that belongs in each space. Circle your answer.

We read a book called *Boom Town*. It takes place in the 1800s. It is about a girl named Amanda. She starts her own business. Ms. Francis told (1) _____ that it is based on a true story. (2) _____ plan to look that up and find out what really happened.

1. A. I
   B. they
   C. we
   D. us

2. E. I
   F. me
   G. us
   H. she

Mom takes us to the library every Saturday morning. I like to walk through the aisles and look at the books. Then I decide which ones to take out. (3) _____ all seem very interesting. I don't know which to read first. I bring (4) _____ home. Then I read the first chapter of each one. That helps me decide the order.

3. A. They
   B. Them
   C. Their
   D. Theirs

4. E. they
   F. them
   G. their
   H. theirs

Jana waited at the line. (5) _____ stretched her muscles. Then she bent down and tied her shoe. She heard the whistle and the race began. Jana ran as fast as she could. It took only seconds. Then (6) _____ feet crossed the finish line. She had won the race!

5. A. She
   B. She's
   C. Her
   D. Her's

6. E. she
   F. she's
   G. her
   H. her's

The bus picks us up every morning at eight o'clock. It (7) _____ empty when we first get on. Then at each stop, another friend gets on. We (8) _____ about everything that happened the night before. I am glad I get to ride the bus.

7. A. am
   B. is
   C. has
   D. have

8. E. talk
   F. talks
   G. talk's
   H. talks'

Our plane landed late last night. I have never been on such a long flight. Then we (9) _____ to wait a long time for our luggage. We watched the circle of bags go around and around. I tried to find (10) _____. Then I jumped forward and grabbed them. At last, it was time to go home!

9. A. has
   B. am
   C. had
   D. is

10. E. our
   F. our's
   G. ours
   H. ours'

We're going camping with our cousins this summer. I can't wait. (11) _____ a lot of fun. They also know a lot about camping. That's important because (12) _____ never actually been camping. I wonder what it'll be like to sleep under the stars.

11. A. They'd
   B. They've
   C. They're
   D. They's

12. E. we'll
   F. we've
   G. we're
   H. we's

© Macmillan/McGraw-Hill

Name _____

- An **adjective** is a word that describes a noun.
- An **adjective** tells *what kind* or *how many*.
    What kind: We looked at the blue house.
    How many: There were two trees in the yard.

Draw one line under each adjective. Draw two lines under the noun that the adjective describes.

1. There is an empty house on our street.

2. We walk by the quiet house daily.

3. I try to look in the dark windows.

4. There are still several bushes in the yard.

5. I saw a big crowd outside the yellow house.

6. Six men were fixing up the old house.

7. I thought I would make a good helper.

8. Many people worked on the pretty house.

9. I learned to hammer long nails.

10. We gave the beautiful house to a family.

11. We planted tall trees in the front.

12. The flat roof no longer leaks.

© Macmillan/McGraw-Hill

 At Home: Have your child make lists of adjectives to describe objects around the house. Have your child use those words in sentences.

Name _____

> • An **adjective** tells *what kind* or *how many*.
> • Use the articles *a* and *an* before singular nouns when referring to something general. Use *a* before a word starting with a consonant. Use *an* before a word starting with a vowel.
> • Use *the* before a singular or plural noun when referring to something specific.

Complete each sentence with an article. Articles may be used more than once.

> a   an   the

1. My family lives in _____ apartment building.

2. We have lived in _____ building for five years.

3. Our building is on _____ nice street.

4. All _____ streets in my neighborhood are lined with trees.

5. My brother and I share _____ room.

6. Our little sister has _____ smallest bedroom.

7. There is _____ orange rug on her bedroom floor.

8. We live near _____ park.

9. _____ park is very beautiful.

10. My best friend lives in _____ blue house nearby.

11. Behind his house is _____ huge yard.

12. After school we play soccer with _____ old ball that I found.

© Macmillan/McGraw-Hill

 At Home: Have your child use the articles and adjectives in the box to create his or her own sentences.

- An **abbreviation** is a shortened form of a word. It begins with a capital letter and ends with a period.
- Capitalize and abbreviate titles before a name:
  Dr. Brown, **Mrs.** Martin, **Mr.** Fox
- Abbreviate "Street" or "Avenue" if they are part of a name or specific address:
  There are many cars on the street today.
  She lives at 21 Ocean **St.**
- Use a comma between the names of a city and state.
- Use a comma between the day and year in a date.

Proofread the business letter. Draw a line through the mistakes and add the correct capitalization and punctuation.

5 Maple street

Morristown nj 07960

April 16 2007

Ms Kim Masters

Acme Builders

441 eagle rock avenue

Roseland NJ 07068

Dear Ms Masters:

   Thank you for meeting with Mister Jones, Doctor Thomas and me yesterday. We liked the house at 2120 riverview street very much. Mr Jones hopes to start repairs on the property in early June. I will call you tomorrow to discuss our plans.

Sincerely yours,

Dr. Mack Frost

Homes for Everyone

© Macmillan/McGraw-Hill

 At Home: Have your child write a letter to a friend or relative who lives far away. Have him or her use correct letter form.

A Castle on Viola Street

163

Book 2/Unit 6

- An **adjective** tells *what kind* or *how many*.
- Use the articles *a* and *an* before singular nouns when referring to something general. Use *a* before a word starting with a consonant. Use *an* before a word starting with a vowel.
- Use *the* before a singular or plural noun when referring to something specific.

Proofread the paragraph. Underline the adjectives. Circle any articles that are used incorrectly.

No one had lived in a old house on Cray Street for a long time. It was in bad shape. The porch sagged. A wall had fallen down inside. Then a community group bought the house. They were going to fix it and give it to an family in town. I helped clean up the rooms. I carried materials to a carpenters. I learned how to measure wood. Best of all, I got to pick out colors for a rooms! Everyone loves the room that I painted.

Rewrite the paragraph. Write the articles correctly. Add any adjectives that will make the paragraph better.

_____

_____

_____

_____

_____

_____

_____

 At Home: Have your child proofread and correct a piece of written homework.

© Macmillan/McGraw-Hill

Name_____

Find the adjective that tells *what kind* or *how many*. Write the adjective on the line.

1. I carried the heavy cans of paint. _____

2. The bright colors spilled out from the can. _____

3. We painted in broad strokes. _____

4. It took time for the wet paint to dry. _____

5. The paint had a soft glow. _____

6. The orange color is on the wall. _____

7. I held the wooden handle of the brush. _____

Decide if *a, an,* or *the* belongs in the sentence. Write your answer on the line.

8. I marked _____ inch on the piece of wood.

9. I looked in the toolbox for _____ saw.

10. Then I began to saw at _____ inch mark.

11. I drew _____ line across the board with a pencil.

12. I carefully cut _____ wood with my saw.

13. I hammered _____ nail in the wood.

14. Then I evened out _____ edges.

15. I closed _____ toolbox.

Name_____

- An **adjective** tells *what kind* or *how many.*
- Use the articles *a* and *an* before singular nouns when referring to something general. Use *a* before a word starting with a consonant. Use *an* before a word starting with a vowel.
- Use *the* before a singular or plural noun when referring to something specific.

Correct each underlined article. Then write the sentences correctly. Insert adjectives before nouns.

1. The house had <u>the</u> coat of paint.

_____

2. Ray planted flowers in front of <u>a</u> porch.

_____

3. Sandy raked leaves off <u>an</u> grass.

_____

4. Bill painted numbers on <u>an</u> mailbox.

_____

Name _____

- Add -er to an adjective to compare two nouns.
- Add -est to an adjective to compare more than two nouns.
  A spider's legs are <u>longer</u> than an ant's legs.
  That is the <u>biggest</u> spider in the barn.

Circle the correct adjective for each sentence.

1. I live in the (quieter, quietest) house on the street.

2. The living room is the (brighter, brightest) room of all.

3. The sun is (warmer, warmest) in that room than anywhere else in the house.

4. It is (cooler, coolest) in the attic than outside in the yard.

5. Our attic is home to the (smaller, smallest) spiders I have ever seen.

6. One spider is (darker, darkest) than the others.

7. This spider here moves (faster, fastest) than that one.

8. It has the (thicker, thickest) legs of all the spiders.

9. One spider web is (higher, highest) than every other web.

10. Its (longer, longest) string reaches all the way down to the floor.

11. I think spiders move (slower, slowest) than ants do.

12. My friend Juan is the (taller, tallest) student in our class.

13. That means I'm (shorter, shortest) than he is.

14. I talk (louder, loudest) than he does, though.

15. We believe the (smarter, smartest) idea is to study every day.

© Macmillan/McGraw-Hill

At Home: Ask your child to make a list of everyday objects at home. Have him or her use adjectives to compare the objects.

Name_____

- In adjectives ending in a consonant and *y*, change the *y* to *i* and add *-er* or *-est*.
- In adjectives ending in *e*, drop the *e* and add *-er* or *-est*.
- In adjectives that have a single vowel before a final consonant, double the final consonant and add *-er* or *-est*.

Change *y* to *i*:	happy	happier	happiest
Drop the *e*:	safe	safer	safest
Double the consonant:	hot	hotter	hottest

Add *-er* or *-est* to each adjective. Write the correct form.

Add *-er*

1. pretty _____
2. blue _____
3. big _____
4. noisy _____
5. red _____

Add *-est*

6. white _____
7. tiny _____
8. pale _____
9. large _____
10. silly _____

Write the correct form of each adjective in parentheses.

6. Charlotte was the (nice) _____ spider anyone knew.

7. The (busy) _____ worker in the barn was Charlotte.

8. Templeton was (lazy) _____ than Wilbur.

9. It was the (wet) _____ day anyone had ever seen.

10. The fair was the (happy) _____ day of Wilbur's life.

 At Home: Ask your child to use the adjectives on this page to compare furniture, clothes, or other items around the house.

Name_____

Adjective	Compares Two	Compares More than Two
good	better	best
bad	worse	worst
many	more	most

Proofread the sentences. Correct adjectives that are misspelled. Then write the sentences correctly.

1. <u>Charlotte's Web</u> is the bestest book I have ever read.

_____

2. Trying to weave a web was Wilbur's baddest idea.

_____

3. I think Charlotte was smarterer than other spiders.

_____

4. With Charlotte's help, Wilbur felt more good than before.

_____

5. My spider bite was worst than yours.

_____

6. That is the more amazing spider I have ever seen.

_____

At Home: Have your child write lines of dialogue where people compare animals they know. Ask him or her to use adjectives with a variety of endings.

Name_____

- Add -*er* to an adjective to compare two nouns and -*est* to compare more than two nouns.
- In adjectives ending in a consonant and *y*, change the *y* to *i* and add -*er* or -*est.*
- In adjectives ending in *e*, drop the *e* and add -*er* or -*est.*
- In adjectives that have a single vowel before a final consonant, double the final consonant and add -*er* or -*est.*

Proofread these lines of dialogue. Circle any adjectives that are incorrectly used or misspelled.

    I remember the worse thing that ever happened to me. I woke up before dawn and couldn't go back to sleep. I turned on the kitchen light and walked through the door. Suddenly, there was something on my face. It was the bigest, scaryiest spider web I had ever seen! I let out the louddest scream I had ever screamed. Then I started to laugh. After all, what was sillyer than getting upset about a spider web?

Rewrite the dialogue. Write the comparative adjectives correctly.

_____

_____

_____

_____

_____

_____

_____

 At Home: Have your child write a paragraph about a scary movie you saw together. Afterwards, have your child proofread the paragraph to correct any mistakes.

Name_____

Read each sentence. Find the sentence that has an adjective that compares. Mark your answer.

1. a. Wilbur sleeps in the barn.
   b. He keeps warm in the straw.
   c. It is darker in the barn than outside.
   d. The moon and stars light the sky.

2. a. Charlotte works in the afternoon.
   b. This is her fanciest web ever.
   c. She writes a strange word in the web.
   d. The strong threads shine in the sun.

3. a. Wilbur thinks he can make a beautiful web.
   b. Templeton ties a long string on Wilbur's tail.
   c. Wilbur falls to the ground.
   d. It is the silliest thing he has ever done.

Read each sentence. Find the correct form of the adjective in parentheses.

4. A spider's silk is (thin) than thread.
   a. thiner
   b. thinner
   c. thiniest
   d. thinniest

5. Pigs are one of the (smart) animals in the world.
   a. smarter
   b. smartter
   c. smarttest
   d. smartest

6. Sometimes dogs are the (hard) working farm animals.
   a. harder
   b. hardst
   c. hardest
   d. harddest

Name_____

- Add -*er* to an adjective to compare two nouns and -*est* to compare more than two nouns.
- In adjectives ending in a consonant and *y*, change the *y* to *i* and add -*er* or -*est*.
- In adjectives ending in *e*, drop the *e* and add -*er* or -*est*.
- In adjectives that have a single vowel before a final consonant, double the final consonant and add -*er* or -*est*.

With a partner, take turns reading each sentence aloud. Rewrite the sentences. Correct the underlined adjectives.

1. Charlotte climbed <u>highest</u> than Wilbur could reach.

   _____

2. She worked in a <u>sunnyer</u> spot than her usual corner.

   _____

3. She spun the <u>longer</u> thread Wilbur had ever seen.

   _____

4. Templeton was the <u>noisier</u> member of the group.

   _____

5. The words in the web were the <u>stranger</u> sight anyone had ever seen.

   _____

   _____

6. Charlotte is the <u>smarter</u> spider I've ever read about.

   _____

7. Charlotte is <u>nice</u> than the spider that bit me.

   _____

8. A spider is much <u>smallest</u> than a pig.

   _____

Name _____

> • An **adverb** is a word that tells more about a verb.
> • Adverbs can tell *where, when,* or *how* an action takes place.

Circle the adverb in each sentence.

1. Before a mission, astronauts prepare for their trip.

2. They work steadily on their tasks.

3. They perform their duties tirelessly.

4. Their space ship flies up.

5. Astronauts must act quickly when they work.

6. They try to perform every experiment correctly.

7. Soon they successfully complete their mission.

8. Then they return to Earth.

9. The astronauts climb down the space ship.

10. Their friends listen excitedly to their adventures.

© Macmillan/McGraw-Hill

 At Home: Have your child look in magazines and newspapers to find pictures. Have your child use some of the adverbs he or she used in the sentences to tell about the pictures.

Name_____

> • Most adverbs that tell *how* an action takes place end in *-ly*
>   **quick + -ly = quickly**
>   Paul walks **slowly.**

Rewrite the sentences. Add *-ly* to the adjective in parentheses to form an adverb.

1. The shuttle launches (swift).

_____

2. The crowd cheers (wild).

_____

3. The astronauts (immediate) get to work.

_____

4. John Glenn checks his heartbeat (careful).

_____

5. The scientists follow his progress (eager).

_____

6. They are (great) excited about the experiments.

_____

7. Some of the shuttle's systems run (automatic).

_____

8. The shuttle runs (perfect).

_____

 At Home: Have your child write three sentences with adverbs to tell about taking a trip or some other family activity.

Name_____

> • An **adjective** is a word that describes a noun.
> • An **adverb** is a word that describes a verb.

Read the sentences below. Circle the word that correctly completes each sentence. Write *adverb* or *adjective* to describe the word you circled.

1. John Glenn is a (great, greatly) American hero.

_____

2. He (bold, boldly) orbited the earth in 1962.

_____

3. It was an (important, importantly) moment in history.

_____

4. In 1998, he volunteered to fly a (second, secondly) mission.

_____

5. He (cheerful, cheerfully) prepared for the flight.

_____

6. Crowds cheered (loud, loudly) during takeoff.

_____

7. The shuttle flew (speedy, speedily) across the blue sky.

_____

8. Everyone (glad, gladly) welcomed the shuttle when it landed.

_____

© Macmillan/McGraw-Hill

 At Home: Have your child use five of the adverbs in these sentences to tell about things that he or she does around the house.

An American Hero Flies Again
Book 2/Unit 6

 175

Name_____

> • An **adverb** is a word that tells more about a verb.
> • Most adverbs that tell *how* an action takes place end in *-ly*.

Proofread the paragraph. Circle any adverbs that are not correct.

    I made my own space shuttle for a science project. I worked endless on it! First, I careful drew a design. Then I cut out pieces of cardboard. The pieces had to fit together perfect. I was sad when some didn't fit exact. But I just went back and tried again. This time everything slid easy into place. I used tape to hold it together secure. Next, I gentle added a string. Then I pulled it rapid through the air. It real looked like it was flying!

Rewrite the paragraph. Write the adverbs correctly.

_____

_____

_____

_____

_____

_____

_____

 At Home: Have your child tell you two things that he or she did quickly and accurately while finishing a school project.

Name_____

Change the word in parentheses to an adverb. Write the adverb on the line.

1. Rockets (powerful) _____ blast the shuttle into the air.

2. Then the rockets (neat) _____ fall away.

3. The shuttle glides (graceful) _____ through space.

4. It lands (smooth) _____ on an airstrip.

5. Soon it (slow) _____ comes to a halt.

6. The crowd cheers (loud) _____.

7. The crew (careful) _____ writes notes.

Underline each adverb.

8. The crew walks swiftly to the shuttle.

9. The crowd greets them wildly.

10. The astronauts wave enthusiastically.

11. The shuttle takes off quickly.

12. The engines roar noisily.

13. The mission goes perfectly.

14. The fans are actually purring.

15. The seatbelts are fastened securely.

Name_____

- An **adverb** is a word that tells more about a verb.
- Most adverbs that tell *how* end in *-ly*. They are formed by adding *-ly* to an adjective.

Read the sentences. Write each underlined adjective correctly as an adverb.

1. At lift-off, the space shuttle seems to move <u>slow</u>. _____

2. But it is <u>actual</u> moving very fast. _____

3. In space, it seems to float <u>graceful</u>. _____

4. Meanwhile, the engines race <u>powerful</u>. _____

5. The winds around Earth roar <u>loud</u>. _____

6. The shuttle astronauts track the wind <u>careful</u>. _____

7. The experiments are running <u>smooth</u>. _____

8. The mission ends <u>perfect</u>. _____

Name _____

> • Some adverbs tell *when* an action takes place.
> • Adverbs that tell when include *first, always, next, after, later, then, soon, early, today, tomorrow, yesterday.*

Draw one line under each adverb that tells *when*. Draw two lines under the verb it describes.

1. Helen and Fred always liked the Bronx Zoo.

2. Soon Helen told Fred he should work there.

3. Today Fred brought home a baby tiger.

4. First, Helen fed the baby tiger with a bottle.

5. Next, she gave him a warm place to sleep.

6. Soon he became big and strong.

7. Rajpur, Dacca, and Raniganj came later.

8. Then they had to go back to the zoo.

9. Helen saw them early in the morning.

10. Tomorrow she will visit them.

11. Now they are seen by many people.

12. Yesterday we saw the baby tigers.

13. We went home later.

14. Next, we did our homework.

15. Let's return soon.

 At Home: Ask your child to write three sentences about a visit to a zoo. Ask him or her to use words that tell *when.*

Name_____

> - Some adverbs tell *where* an action takes place.
> - Adverbs that tell where include *there, outside, up, here,*
>   *nearby, ahead, around, far, away, everywhere.*

Draw one line under each adverb that tells where. Draw two lines under the verb it describes.

1. The baby tigers didn't live outside.

2. They played inside.

3. The tigers roamed everywhere.

4. They didn't go far from Helen, though.

5. She stayed nearby and watched them.

6. Dacca saw the curtains and climbed up.

7. Rajpur crawled around the sofa.

8. Raniganj jumped ahead of the others.

9. Finally, the tigers go away to the zoo.

10. Helen and Fred moved the tigers there.

11. They do not always stay inside.

12. I have been here before.

13. The tigers went everywhere with them.

14. The zoo was not far from my school.

15. We walked around the zoo.

At Home: Have your child write two questions about pets that begin with *Where*. Then have him or her answer the questions with a one-word response such as *Here* or *Away*.

Name_____

> - Some words are used to help introduce a sentence. These words include *well, yes, no, in fact, first, however, therefore*.
> - Use a comma after introductory words.
>   Yes, I am going to the party.
>   In fact, I'll be the first person there.

Rewrite each sentence. Add a comma after the introductory words in the sentences.

1. Yes we did enjoy our vacation.

_____

2. No we did not go rafting.

_____

3. However we did get a chance to visit a zoo.

_____

4. Well I think I liked the baby tigers the best.

_____

5. First we watched them sleeping.

_____

6. Therefore it wasn't very exciting.

_____

7. However we came back later and they were playing.

_____

8. In fact that was my favorite part of the visit.

_____

 At Home: Have your child write four sentences that begin with *Yes* or *No*, each telling how he or she took care of a pet or friend today.

Name_____

> • Some adverbs tell *when* an action takes place.
> • Some adverbs tell *where* an action takes place.

Proofread these paragraphs. Circle adverbs that tell *when* or *where*.

Today we met a zookeeper. Her name is Meg. Early in the day, Meg gave us a tour of the zoo. First we went outside. We saw the workers feed the animals there. Ahead we saw a sign for the nursery. We went inside. The zoo takes care of the baby tigers here. Two baby tigers arrived yesterday. They are awake now. It is fun to see them close to us. Wow it's late. Therefore we must go soon. However tomorrow I will look for books about baby tigers.

Writing Activity

Rewrite the paragraph. Add commas after introductory words.

_____

_____

_____

_____

_____

_____

_____

_____

_____

_____

_____

At Home: Have your child add two or more sentences to this paragraph. Each sentence should contain an adverb that tells *where* or *when.*

© Macmillan/McGraw-Hill

Name

Choose the word in each sentence that is an adverb.

1. Today Fred brought home a baby tiger for Helen to help.
   - **a.** Today
   - **b.** brought
   - **c.** baby
   - **d.** help

2. Helen stayed nearby and watched the tiger sleep.
   - **a.** stayed
   - **b.** nearby
   - **c.** watched
   - **d.** sleep

**Decide which word in the sentence is a adverb that tells *when*.
Mark your answer.**

3. First, the tigers slept there in the little box.
   - **a.** First
   - **b.** slept
   - **c.** there
   - **d.** little

4. Fred and Helen will take them to live outside at the zoo soon.
   - **a.** take
   - **b.** outside
   - **c.** zoo
   - **d.** soon

**Decide which word in the sentence is an adverb that tells *where*.
Mark your answer.**

5. Today one of the tigers wandered away.
   - **a.** Today
   - **b.** one
   - **c.** wandered
   - **d.** away

6. Then Helen found him outside.
   - **a.** Then
   - **b.** Helen
   - **c.** found
   - **d.** outside

Name

- Some adverbs tell *when* an action takes place.
- Some adverbs tell *where* an action takes place.

Mechanics

- Some words are used to help introduce a sentence. These words include *well, yes, no, in fact, first, however, therefore*.
- Use a comma after introductory words.

Rewrite these sentences. Underline the adverbs that tell *where* or *when*. Put commas after any introductory words.

1. First we saw the tigers sleeping.

_____

2. Well one tiger looked up.

_____

3. In fact he turned around and stared at me!

_____

4. However there was a zookeeper ahead with food.

_____

5. Yes the tiger was looking there at him.

_____

6. No, the tiger was not near me.

_____

Name_____

> • Two sentences that tell about the same person, place, or thing can be combined by adding an **adjective** to one sentence.
>
>   The caterpillar crawled along the leaf. The caterpillar is fuzzy.
>
>   The fuzzy caterpillar crawled along the leaf.

Combine each pair of sentences by adding an adjective to one sentence. Write the new sentence on the line.

1. A chrysalis hangs from the branch.

The chrysalis is green.

_____

2. A butterfly moves inside the chrysalis.

It is a colorful butterfly.

_____

3. The butterfly splits the chrysalis.

It is an adult butterfly.

_____

4. The butterfly moves its wings.

The wings are strong.

_____

5. Now the butterfly soars into the sky.

The butterfly is lovely.

_____

 At Home: Have your child list five adjectives that tell about butterflies or other insects.

Home-Grown Butterflies **185**
Book 2/Unit 6

Name_____

> • Two sentences that tell about the same action can be
>   combined by adding an **adverb** to one sentence.
>   The butterfly lands on my finger. It lands neatly.
>   The butterfly lands neatly on my finger.

**Combine each pair of sentences by adding an adverb to one
sentence. Write the new sentence on the line.**

1. We enter the butterfly room.

   We enter quietly.

   _____

2. A butterfly brushes against my face.

   It brushes gently.

   _____

3. Tim reaches for a butterfly.

   He reaches quickly.

   _____

4. The butterfly darts away.

   It darts speedily.

   _____

5. The butterfly's wings echo through the room.

   They echo softly.

   _____

 At Home: Have your child write one pair of sentences like the
ones in this lesson. Then have your child write a third sentence
that contains all the important information in the sentence pair.

Name _____

> • Use commas to separate three or more words in a series.
> • Use a comma after introductory words.
> • Use a comma in a compound sentence.
> • Use a comma after the greeting and closing of a letter.

Rewrite the letter on the lines below. Correct any missing commas.

Dear Caroline

    How are you? We went to see a special butterfly exhibit and I learned many things. It's in a glass house in a garden. The glass and sun keep the house heated. The butterflies need the warmth. First caterpillars form a chrysalis. They turn into butterflies inside. The butterflies split the chrysalis pump their wings and take off. Afterward, they fly around inside the glass house.

                        Your friend
                        Tina

_____

_____

_____

_____

_____

_____

_____

_____

At Home: Have your child look through pages of a book or magazine. Ask him or her to find examples of each kind of comma use.

Name_____

- Two sentences that tell about the same person, place, or thing can be combined by adding an adjective to one sentence.
- Two sentences that tell about the same action can be combined by adding an adverb to one sentence.

Proofread the paragraph. Find and underline the pairs of sentences that can be combined.

    The butterfly swooped down from the sky. It swooped gracefully. It landed on Mom's lilac bush. It landed gently. It was a bush of purple lilacs. I walked over to it. I walked quietly. I wanted to see it up close. The butterfly was mostly yellow. It was a pale yellow. It had black marks around the edges of its wings. The wings looked like they were made of velvet feathers. They looked soft. I sketched the butterfly. I quickly sketched. Then I went inside and looked it up. It was a Tiger Swallowtail.

Writing Activity

Rewrite the paragraph with the combined sentences.

_____

_____

_____

_____

_____

_____

_____

_____

At Home: Have your child write a description of something nice he or she saw happen in a park or garden. Invite your child to send the description in a letter to a family member who was not present.

© Macmillan/McGraw-Hill

Name_____

Underline the adjective that can be used to combine each pair of sentences. Then combine the sentences.

1. Jeff ran from the bumblebee.
It was a furry bumblebee.

_____

2. Jane watched the ants.
They were busy ants.

_____

3. The butterfly beat its wings.
They were strong wings.

_____

4. The butterfly landed on a branch.
It was a thin branch.

_____

5. It searched the sky for birds.
The birds are hungry.

_____

Underline the adverb that can be used to combine each pair of sentences. Then combine the sentences.

6. The firefly glowed.
It glowed brightly.

_____

7. The dragonfly hummed.
It hummed loudly.

_____

8. The breeze blew over the pond.
The breeze blew gently.

_____

© Macmillan/McGraw-Hill

Name_____

- Two sentences that tell about the same person, place, or thing can be combined by adding an adjective to one sentence.
- Two sentences that tell about the same action can be combined by adding an adverb to one sentence.

Mechanics

- Use a comma between the name of a city and a state.
- Use a comma between the day and the year in a date.
- Use commas to separate three or more words in a series.
- Use a comma after introductory words.
- Use a comma in a compound sentence.
- Use a comma after the greeting and closing of a letter.

Read the letter. On a separate sheet of paper, rewrite the letter and put commas where they belong. Also, write each pair of underlined sentences as one sentence.

2 Birch Street
Locust Grove MA 02134
March 24 2006

Dear Aunt Keri

   A butterfly flew into my room. It was black and orange. The butterfly was beautiful. It fluttered around the room. It fluttered quickly. It landed on the desk the chair and my hand! Finally it flew out the window. I am sending you a picture I drew of me and the butterfly.

   Well I hope to see you soon.

Love
Maria

© Macmillan/McGraw-Hill

Read the passages and look at the underlined parts. Is there a better way to write each part? If there is, which is the better way? Mark your answer.

   I decided to change my room. (1) The walls were an dull green. I picked out new paint. Now my room is bright blue. I had too much stuff on the floor. I moved my furniture. I put up new shelves. (2) It has most space for playing. I like it a lot better now.

1. **A** The walls, they were a green.
   B The walls were a green dull.
   C The walls were a dull green.
   D No mistake

2. **E** It has more space for playing.
   F It has more playing.
   G It has space for most playing.
   H No mistake

   Everyone thinks my brothers and I are exactly alike. However, that's not true at all. Jake is an inch taller than I am. (3) Sam's hair is light than Jake's. Jake is good at every sport. Sam likes math. (4) As for me, well, I'm the funniest by far!

3. **A** Sam's hair is lightter than Jake's.
   B Sam's hair is lighter than Jake's.
   C Sam's hair is lightest than Jake's.
   D No mistake.

4. **E** As for me, well, I'm the funnier by far!
   F As for me, well, I'm the funnyest by far!
   G As for me, well, I'm the funnyiest by far!
   H No mistake.

(5) I usual take my dog Star for a walk every morning. I say hi to all my neighbors. Star stops to play with other dogs who are also out walking. When he sees a butterfly or a bird, he jumps into the air. (6) He twists sudden and turns and barks. Then he rolls around on the grass. He's a very funny dog.

5. **A** I take usual my dog Star for a walk a morning.
   B I usually take my dog Star for a walk every morning.
   C I take my usual dog Star for a walk yesterday morning.
   D No mistake

6. **E** He sudden twists and turns and barks.
   F He twists and turns and barks sudden.
   G He twists suddenly and turns and barks.
   H No mistake

Sophie sat down at the piano. (7) She cleared her throat. She cleared it nervously. Then she began to play. (8) The music filled the theater. The music was beautiful. When she finished, she stood up and bowed. Everyone clapped for her.

7. **A** She cleared her throat nervously.
   B She cleared her throat and nervously.
   C She cleared her throat. It cleared nervously.
   D No mistake.

8. **E** The beautiful music, in the theater.
   F The beautiful music filled the theater.
   G The music filled the theater and it was beautiful.
   H No mistake.

© Macmillan/McGraw-Hill